Forests of Central and Southern Scotland

by HERBERT L. EDLIN, B.Sc.

Forestry Commission

EDINBURGH

HER MAJESTY'S STATIONERY OFFICE

1969

Loch Rannoch and Schiehallion. An easterly view over the vast Rannoch Forest in central Perthshire.

Foreword

The region covered by this booklet is the southern third of Scotland, from the headwaters of the Tay in Perthshire, down to the Border. It holds the two great cities of Edinburgh and Glasgow, the widespread industries that have been built up over the central coalfields, the richest farmlands and also—rather surprisingly—one-third of Scotland's forests and woodlands.

Because they lie so close at hand, these are the woods most often seen and visited by resident and tourist alike. Most of this text is planned to show how best you can find and appreciate the woodlands of each county, while the photos provide a record of their unrivalled scenery and surroundings. But these forests are not simply lovely to look at. They have a long history and a well-planned future, both firmly linked with Scotland's economy. It is fascinating to trace their origin from the remote past, and to see why people go on planting trees for the changed needs of today.

Loch Tummel. Looking south-west from the Killiecrankie-Rannoch road, over Faskally Forest, to Meall Tarneachan.

Contents

ACKNOWLEDGMENTS

The cover picture, title page view, and Plates 4, 23, 24, 25, 26, 35, 42, 43 and 44 are the work of the Commission's own photographic staff, led by Mr. I. A. Anderson.

Thanks are also due to the following photographers, for providing the pictures listed: Mr. F. G. Sykes for views on pages ii and iv, and Plates 7, 8, 13, 14 and 36. Mr. K. M. Andrew for Plates 5 and 6. Mr. B. R. Feaver for the view on page vi and Plate 46. Mr. L. S. Paterson for Plates 1, 9, 19, 20 and 27. Valdemars Blankenburgs for Plates 2, 3 and 41. *The Scotsman* for Plates 10, 12, 17, 18, 37, 38. Tom Weir for Plates 11, 16 and 21. Douglas Scott for Plate 15. Mr. R. N. Lochhead for Plate 22. Mr. A. D. S. Macpherson for Plates 28, 29, 30 and 34. Leonard and Marjorie Gayton for Plate 31. David Innes for Plate 32. Fox Photos for Plate 33. Geoffrey Wright for Plate 39. David Wilkie for Plate 40. Robert M. Adam for Plate 45.

The maps are based, by permission, on the Ordnance Survey, and were adapted by the Commission's Cartographic Staff and Studio Corot, London.

The cover picture shows Loch Faskally in Faskally Forest, north of Pitlochry, Perthshire. The title page shows a view over Kirroughtree Forest Nursery, near Newton Stewart, to the uplands of Glen Trool Forest Park, Galloway.

Scots pines in Black Wood, Rannoch Forest. Native Caledonian strains of varied form, with Loch Rannoch beyond.

1. Historical

Ancient Forests

About 9,000 years ago, the ice sheets that had for long held Scotland in their grip began to melt and dwindle away. As the ice receded, the ground warmed up, and was invaded first by low arctic-alpine plants that still survive, as occasional rarities, on the tops of our higher mountains, and then by moorland plants that remain familiar to everyone today—heather and bilberry, sphagnum moss, deer grass, cotton grass, and a host of commoner grasses and rushes. Following these came the first hardy trees—birch, pine, juniper and rowan, which are still characteristic of the higher braes and the more northerly counties. In their wake came less hardy sorts, oak and ash, wych elm and alder, to take their places lower down in the dales and glens, particularly in the south and east. We know a great deal about this progression because the pollen of each kind of plant and tree can be identified in a preserved state at different levels in the peat bogs. All these trees, now regarded as natives, entered Scotland overland from England, to which country they had gained entry by means of a land bridge—now vanished—from continental Europe.

We cannot draw an accurate picture of the great forest that occupied Scotland for several thousands of years before the Christian era. The peat bogs tell us roughly *what* trees grew, but they do not define the *extent* of the woods; this probably varied widely, in extent and altitude up the hills, according to changes in climate. The continued existence of the peat bogs themselves shows that not all the lowland was wooded, and though the upper limit of tree growth may sometimes have exceeded the present figure of 2,000 feet, the rocky upper slopes of bens over 3,000 feet in height can never have carried real woodland, even when the climate was better.

The peat bogs show that many treeless hills below 2,000 feet were once clad in forest—for stumps of birch and pine are frequently exposed by peat cutters for all to see. Perhaps as much as half of Scotland's broken and rugged land surface once bore natural forest, the rest being mountain, moor and bog. That would be 50 per cent, as compared with 10 per cent today. So the woods are now only about one-fifth as extensive as they were in prehistoric times.

A possible origin of Scotland's ancient name of Caledonia, is the Gaelic *coille dun*, meaning "the wooded heights". The Romans well knew the wildness of the *Silva Caledonis* or great forest of Caledonia, inhabited by unsubdued Celtic tribes. In later times, the term "Caledonian forest" has often been applied purely to the Highlands, and even to woods of Scots pine alone; but originally it meant all the land north of Hadrian's Wall, which stretched from the Solway to the Tyne.

The trees that formed this native forest are familiar today, for fragments of natural wood survive. The commonest were the birches, which ranged farthest north and highest up the hills. Three species—the silver birch, *Betula pendula*, the white birch, *B. pubescens*, and the dwarf birch, *B. nana*—all grow wild in Scotland. Birches renew their kind more readily than other trees and spread by windborne seed without the aid of the forester, especially where woodland is cleared by felling or by fire. Some birchwoods are true relics of the past; others are of recent, though still natural, origin.

Growing amid the birches was the Scots pine, *Pinus sylvestris*. Foresters call it "Scots pine", a name proposed by Sir Walter Scott, to show its affinities with other pines, as well as its native status: but it is found throughout western Europe, while in Scotland it is still commonly known by its older name of "fir" or "Scots fir".

Many fragments of old pinewoods survive in the Highlands, from Argyll and Perthshire to Sutherland and Banff, illustrating the ancient spread of this magnificent tree. Farther south there are few undisputed relics left, but there is abundant evidence from pollen and timber in peat bogs to show that Scots pine was once common right to the Border. Scots pine was the first conifer to be planted in Scotland for its timber; many splendid crops have been raised, and it is still widely planted today.

Three other conifers are undoubted natives, namely the yew, *Taxus baccata*, and two bushy junipers:—*Juniperus communis*, the common juniper, and *J. nana*, the dwarf juniper. None has any timber value.

Oaks followed, and became established on the low ground right through Scotland, except the extreme north. Both the two common kinds are found; the sessile oak, *Quercus petraea*, takes the lead in the north

PLATE I Border river: the Annan seen through a screen of ash foliage, below Lockerbie, Dumfries-shire.

and west, and the pedunculate oak, *Q. robur*, is more common elsewhere. Native oaks remain leading trees in the centre, south, and west, but because most of the natural oakwoods have been cut over in the past for firewood, charcoal, and bark for tanning leather, many are now little more than scrub. Planted oakwoods in the lowlands yield excellent timber.

The wych or Scots elm, *Ulmus glabra*, was frequent in the south and it remains a leading tree in the half-wild woods of Border dales and glens. Alder, *Alnus glutinosa*, grew along streamsides and on damp hillsides, while ash, *Fraxinus excelsior*, and aspen, *Populus tremula*, were found on fertile ground all the way to the far north. Among the lesser trees, the rowan, *Sorbus aucuparia*, was common and grew at quite high elevations, while local races of white-beams, such as *Sorbus scandica*, grew here and there.

In the glens, especially in the north, there flourished the beautiful little bird cherry, *Prunus padus*. Both the hawthorns, *Crataegus monogyna* and *C. oxyacanthoides*, and the blackthorn or sloe, *Prunus spinosa*, were common. There were many kinds of willows, of the genus *Salix*, ranging from dwarf forms or prostrate creepers growing high up in the mountains to osiers and goat willows in glens and dales. The shrubby hazel, *Corylus avellana*, formed thickets below taller trees, while the elder or bore-tree, *Sambucus nigra*, is also native. Untended by the hand of the forester, these trees of the ancient Caledonian Forest grew to their prime, and scattered the seeds from which fresh seedlings sprang up. They had many natural enemies—deer browsed them back and they fell victims to fungal diseases or insect pests just as trees do today. But other forces of nature assisted them—wolves and foxes kept down the numbers of the deer, and even the insect pests had their own peculiar enemies to keep them in check. Enough saplings survived to renew, and even to extend, the green forest cover. Until mankind appeared on the scene the trees held sway over mile after mile of hill and glen.

The Great Woods Decline

The vast Forest of Caledonia diminished steadily down the centuries, to reach its lowest ebb in the mid-eighteenth century. About 10 million acres of pine, birch, and oakwood was reduced to bare moor and mountainside. Many reasons put forward for this decline can be dismissed as more picturesque than accurate. History is often a record of violent events, and it is natural to link forest destruction with them, but a more scientific review shows that little connection exists. It is said, for example, that the forests were cut down on a wholesale scale because they harboured wolves, robber bands or outlaws, or because they hindered the operations of one army or another during the wars with England. Great fires or terrific gales are also called in to account for the sudden disappearance of woods on a

catastrophic scale. There is no doubt that such drastic events did play some part in the diminution of the tree cover, but a moment's reflection will show that, taken in isolation, they could hardly account for the known march of events. For this forest was a natural one, and if ever it were to be devastated by some isolated catastrophe, it would soon rebuild itself by the same processes of growth that had first given it birth.

The explanation lies readily at hand in the normal processes of husbandry, exercised throughout the land by the countryfolk over the course of three or four thousand years. These can be summed up in three operations—grazing, muirburn, and clearance for tillage.

Wherever livestock are kept in a reasonable density on the ground, their grazing destroys the young seedling trees; if this grazing pressure is kept up for a sufficient number of years, there are no young saplings to replace the old trees that eventually die and fall. Thus a whole forest may slowly vanish without anyone raising an axe; for the trees are felled at an earlier and more vulnerable stage by a finer but equally efficient instrument—the sheep's tooth. Since the sheep cover the ground repeatedly year after year, there is no chance of a new forest arising after the old one has gone. It was also the practice to cut natural hay wherever it could be found, for winter keep; so the mower's scythe killed off countless small trees.

Muirburn is a process associated with grazing, and consists in the burning away of dead vegetation—heather, bracken, gorse, and coarse grass—during the dry months of spring. The object is to encourage the early growth of fresh green grass and heather, so as to give the livestock an "early bite" when pasturage is scarce. In the long run muirburn impoverishes the soil, but it meets the graziers's immediate need, and therefore it has long been practised throughout the Scottish hills. It destroys, inevitably, any young trees exposed to the fury of the flames.

Clearance for tillage affected a relatively small part of Scotland's land surface, for the country still holds great expanses of moor and mountain that have never known the plough—being too infertile, steep, or rocky. But in the broad vales and straths, and along the seaboard, it was responsible for the gradual disappearance of the woods. Such clearance yielded much useful timber and firewood, and so delayed the day when it became necessary to exploit the more distant forests of the hills.

The cutting of timber for sale played only a minor part in the destruction of the woods, for it was not until the eighteenth century that an export trade to England was developed, or industry and building in the Scottish towns began to call for large supplies. By that time, the woods had already been diminished by other causes. Thereafter, throughout the nineteenth century, imports of timber to Scotland from Scandinavia, Russia and America grew in volume and few heavy inroads were made into native timber stocks until the severe overcutting of the 1914–18 and 1939–45 wars.

The harvesting of firewood did little harm to the forests, for there was for long abundant branchwood from the timber trees that were removed during clearance for tillage. The declining forests of the uplands, menaced by grazing, also provided a good store of firewood as their old trees matured, decayed, and fell. When trees became more scarce, a system of rotational cutting was introduced, on many estates, to safeguard firewood supplies, while in the treeless regions people eventually turned to coal or peat. A change of land use, from forest to grazings and arable lands, was responsible for the loss of most of the Scottish woodland. This took place so gradually that it was almost unperceived. From time to time orders were made for the exclusion of cattle, goats, and sheep from the woods, and this shows that the landowners were aware of the danger to the trees; but these orders were seldom observed for long.

Farming in Scotland was developed by people of varied origins who came from abroad. First there were the Neolithic or New Stone Age men whose settlements have been revealed by the spade of the archaeologist at such places as Skara Brae in the Orkneys, then the Celtic Picts and Scots, of whom we have historical records, and at length the Angles of the Lothians and the Borders, and the Norsemen who settled around the coast, in many Border dales, and in the northern and western isles. A common feature of all early husbandry was a dependence on livestock—all these settlers were pastoralists who depended largely on flocks and herds for the essentials of life—meat, hides, wool, butter and cheese; tillage, involving the growing of oats and barley in small fields, needed relatively little land. Each community developed its grazings on a simple plan— the inbye land near the arable land of the village, and the extensive common grazings of the mountains and moors around. From claims to such widespread grazing stem many of the territorial divisions that survive today —such as parish and county boundaries, the marches of estates, the "commonties" of the crofting townships, the broad divisions into districts like Kyle or the Merse, and even the limits of territories ascribed to Highland clans or Border families.

Herdsmen

For the effective grazing of the upland or outlying pastures, it was essential to take the beasts to centres away from the townships during the long summer days when the grass grew green on the hills. The younger herdsmen and milkmaids went with them, leaving the older folk behind. This is called the shieling system, from the Norse words *skale* and *skjol* for a temporary summer abode; these words survive, often in the form of *shiel*, in scores of place names. In Gaelic a shieling was called *airidh*, often spelt in place names as *arie*. Some of the Border shielings were called "bughts", a word drawn from the Norse *buth*, a dwelling, and allied to Scots "bothy"; nowadays a bught is just a sheep-fold. This method of using the summer grazings was common throughout Scotland, from the Borders to the Hebrides, as ample legends, traditions, records, and folk songs testify; it continued on the hills of Banff until 1870.

The importance of this shieling system to Scotland's forest history lies in its effects on upland tree cover. It provided a multitude of centres from which sheep, cattle, goats, and ponies exercised grazing pressure on the young trees; this was most serious high up the hills, where the trees regenerate least readily. In those days ewes were milked in summer, and goats were kept in great numbers. Around each bothy where the young folk lived in summer the animals ranged and gradually destroyed the young trees, until at length the clearings joined up and a bare hillside resulted. When this happened, the grazings lost much of their value, since there was no shelter. By then the system was in decline—and there was a general move to convert the uplands into sheep walks or deer "forests"—forests now in little more than name, though preserving the title gained when they were thick with trees. The people who once frequented the shielings vanished in the general scheme of Highland and upland "clearances"—going away to the low grounds, the cities, or far overseas. Much of the scant store of fertility found on the hills disappeared with the tree cover, and plants of low feeding value, such as deer grass, heather, and bog mosses, took the place of the sweeter forest grasses and herbage.

The steeper and rockier slopes of the hills proved least attractive to grazing animals, so it is there that we still find the few surviving natural woods. The sessile oak has hung on to hillsides in central and western Scotland, hazel survives in Argyll and wych elm in the Border cleughs, birch scrub persists on rough braes strewn with boulders or scree, and alder occurs in marshy places unattractive to animals. The native woods of Scots pine lie mostly on the sunless and least attractive southern side of steep glens. Scotland's native woods are now found, not in the places best suited to trees, but in the places least suited to grazing.

This slow business of whittling away the natural forest cover ran its course to its logical conclusion—a treeless landscape—most rapidly in the Lowlands and the Borders. There real concern was felt for the lack of timber as early as the fifteenth century, when there was still ample pine, oak, and birch over much of the Highlands. Communications were poor and there was real difficulty in carrying timber and fuel over long distances. So we have the paradox of people actively planting trees in one part of the country while their contemporaries were passively permitting forest destruction in another.

As time went on and the firm ownership of land by

the lairds became established, they found it possible to let the old forest lands to sheep farmers for money rents. This happened on a grand scale in the Borders after their pacification through the Union of the Crowns in 1603; most of the resulting sheep walks remain. It happened in the Highlands after the 1745 rebellion, but there the land proved less kind; after a brief spell of sheep grazing most of it degenerated into deer forest and grouse moor, with a residual value as a sporting wilderness rather than a pastoral countryside. Both these movements were accompanied by the wholesale "clearances" of the people who had once claimed the land as their own. When we look upon these wastes today we must reflect that the removal of their trees was first achieved by a population far more numerous than now exists. Two or three shepherds suffice to tend flocks on sheepwalks that once carried scores of crofts and a thriving population.

The pioneers of large-scale sheep farming for the produce of wool for export were the Cistercian and Benedictine monks, who first appeared in Scotland at Melrose Abbey in 1136. The main pastoral monastic centres were: Melrose, Jedburgh, Glenluce in Wigtownshire, Sweetheart Abbey near Dumfries, Newbattle in Midlothian, Kinloss near Forres, Coupar Angus in Perthshire, Balmerino and Culross in Fife, Deer in Aberdeenshire, Dunfermline, Kelso and Arbroath; but there were many smaller centres too. Each of the larger monasteries sent out to graze, with the help of lay brethren established in outlying granges, anything from 3,000 to 12,500 sheep. They were able to do this because successive kings and nobles gave them perpetual grants of forest land. The wool crop, shipped overseas to Holland and Italy, was a continuing source of wealth to the monasteries, and enabled them to build those splendid abbeys that now stand—with few exceptions—in ruins. The charters of the abbeys form a valuable contemporary source of information on forests and farming. For 400 years, from 1150 to 1550 A.D., the monks continued this profitable large-scale grazing, time enough for large expanses of woodland to be reduced to grassland and moor. Then, with the Reformation, their lands passed into secular hands, and the business of sheep-farming was continued by lairds and farmers.

Hunters

Throughout the Middle Ages the diminishing forests were also used as hunting grounds by the Scottish kings and nobles, who introduced forest laws and appointed hereditary keepers on the lines of England and Continental countries. They aimed to maintain enough deer and other large game, such as wild boar, for the royal sport of hunting. To allow for this, the number of cattle and sheep that might be kept in the king's forests was, in theory, restricted. Poaching was rife, and despite picturesque enactments and dire penalties, few Scots ever feared to take a salmon from the river or a deer from the hill. The wild red and roe deer, exposed to both wolves and human hunters—long remained too few to do much harm to seedling trees. With the sheep, which were guarded against both human and animal marauders, it was another matter.

Forest Laws, enacted by King William (1165–1214), once excluded sheep and goats from the royal woods entirely, and permitted swine to enter only when there was an abundant crop of acorns for them to eat. But the same laws allowed cattle to be pastured except for a month oddly defined as "fifteen days on either side of the feast of St. John the Baptist" (24th June); the purpose of this exclusion was to allow the deer to drop their fawns without disturbance. The cutting of timber was forbidden, under penalty of a fine of eight cows, and so was the harvesting of hay. Owners of mastiffs and greyhounds were looked upon with suspicion, and there were stern penalties both for hunting the king's deer and for poaching in other men's woods. Hares, rabbits, game birds and their eggs, all received legal, if not actual, protection. Rooks were looked upon with distrust, and the unfortunate owner of a rookery was liable to forfeit to the king the trees in which they nested. As a final picturesque touch:

"The Schirefs and Barons suld hunt the Wolf foure or thrie times in the year, betwixt St. Mark's day and Lambes (Lammas), quilk is the time of their quhelpes. And the tenants sall rise with them . . . ."

Examples of Royal Forests in Scotland are Glenartney in Perthshire, Kincardine in Kincardineshire, Stocket close to Aberdeen and Dalness in Argyll. The Queen's Park next to the royal palace of Holyroodhouse in Edinburgh is another survival, but the old Scottish forest laws are now a dead letter.

Planting Lairds

From 1457 on, the Scottish Parliament passed many Acts for the encouragement of tree planting. Had these Acts been generally observed Scotland would soon have regained much of its lost woodland cover, but it is obvious from the subsequent course of events that everything depended on the interest—or otherwise—of each individual proprietor.

By an Act of 1457 all freeholders were required to plant trees near their steadings, hedges round their fields and "broom parks" for shelter and winter fodder; tenants were also required to plant so many trees each year. Another Act, in 1504, went further, saying:

"It is statute and ordanit anent policy to be halden in the cuntre that everilk lord and laird make thame to have parkis with deer, stankis, cunyngaris, dowcatis, heggis, and plant at least ane aker of wod quhare thair is na greit woodis nor forestis."

In other words, every laird was obliged by law to establish deer parks, fish ponds, rabbit warrens, dovecotes, and hedges and, if he lived in a treeless region, to plant at least one acre of woodland.

Although such enactments were followed only spasmodically in the Lowlands, and scarcely at all in the Highlands, they do provide evidence of organised afforestation at an early date. We need not take seriously the gibes of the well-known English traveller, Dr. Samuel Johnson, who declared that, in 1773, the Lowlands were treeless. There is abundant contemporary evidence of tree planting going on, on every hand, in the regions through which he travelled, though no doubt the bare Border hills gave a deep impression of a naked landscape to a traveller from the south.

One of the earliest of the planting lairds was Sir Duncan Campbell, also known as "Black Duncan of the Seven Castles", who established plantations of oak, birch, and Scots pine on Drummond Hill in Perthshire, between 1582 and 1631. During the years 1613 and 1614 he was also active in Glenorchy, where he made enclosures for raising pine, oak, ash, birch and the plane tree or sycamore. He supplied his farm tenants with trees from his nurseries, declared penalties for damage to trees, and made rules for the conduct of muirburn, which he recognised as a major threat to plantations. In 1637, his successor, Sir Colin Campbell, sent Scots pine seed to a certain Lady Hamilton, for her son to grow on her estates; later he also sent seed to that great diarist and tree planter, John Evelyn, author of the classic work *Silva*, who planted the resulting pines on his estate at Wotton in Surrey. Another early enthusiast for tree planting was the Sixth Earl of Haddington, who planted 800 acres of woods on his estate of Tyninghame in East Lothian, between 1700 and 1735, and left a detailed account of the methods he used.

On the Atholl estates in Central Perthshire, the Second Duke of Atholl began, in 1740, the extensive cultivation of the European larch, an introduced tree previously little planted. This work was expanded by the Fourth Duke, nicknamed "Planter John", who planted no less than 10,000 acres of larch between 1774 and 1830. He used 15 million young larch trees, nearly all of which were raised from seed in his estate nurseries.

These Atholl enterprises were the largest in Scotland, but afforestation on a smaller scale was proceeding simultaneously on scores of other estates throughout the country. The first *Statistical Account of Scotland*, published in 1792, includes abundant accounts of such work, compiled by the parish ministers who were in close touch with the lairds and foresters. They reveal a widespread interest in afforestation. The *Second Statistical Account*, published around 1845, shows the great estate plantation movement continuing unabated. Towards the end of the nineteenth century it lost some of its force and drive, but by then it had resulted in the establishment of 750,000 acres of timber.

The planting of trees by the lairds on their private estates followed a common pattern throughout Scotland. Their objects were fourfold:

First, to grow timber, largely for use on their own properties.

Second, to provide shelter for their houses, gardens, home farms, and fields.

Third, to provide cover for game.

Fourth, to improve their estates from the landscape or scenic point of view, and provide privacy for house and garden.

Woods which fulfil these needs are known in Scotland as "policies", a word of French origin which signifies managed woods; they correspond broadly to the parks around English mansions. They have usually been established on fertile ground, for each proprietor's house and farm had naturally been established on the best land available to him. He did not mind giving up some of his arable ground to trees, in return for the advantages that they brought; in particular the shelter they gave improved the yields from his crops and livestock.

New Trees from Far Lands

The trees grown in the policies were at first only those native to the country—oak, ash, birch, pine and willow were certainly used. But beech, *Fagus sylvatica*, was brought from England at early date; it was being planted at Newbattle about 1550. Sycamore, *Acer pseudoplatanus*, introduced direct from France, was also planted in Tudor times—Mary Queen of Scots is said to have planted a sycamore at Little France, south of Edinburgh. It became known throughout Scotland, both in tree and timber form, as "plane", which is apt to cause confusion now with the other planes of the genus *Platanus*. The little Scots laburnum, *Laburnum anagyroides*, from Central Europe, was also planted for its timber early on. It was followed later by many evergreen undershrubs intended for shelter and game cover, especially the common rhododendron, *Rhododendron ponticum* from Asia Minor, and the cherry laurel, *Prunus laurocerasus*, from the Mediterranean shores.

Other early introductions were those of lime trees, *Tilia* species, to Taymouth in 1664; black poplar, *Populus nigra*, to Hamilton in 1696; horse chestnut, *Aesculus hippocastunum*, to New Posso in 1709; English elm, *Ulmus procera*, to Dalmahoy in 1763; and Norway maple, *Acer platanoides*, to Mountstewart by 1738.

Sweet chestnut, *Castanea sativa*, was grown in 1691, and walnut, *Juglans regia*, in 1696, both on the estate of Sir John Foulis of Ravelston, Midlothian. At Urie in Kincardineshire, in 1682, the tenants, who received plants from the estate nursery, had to plant so many ashes, sycamores, birches, and pines every year, as well as rowans, *Sorbus aucuparia*, and geans or wild cherries, *Prunus avium*. At Monymusk, Aberdeenshire, in 1723, Sir Archibald Grant was raising Dutch elm, *Ulmus* species, hornbeam, *Carpinus betulus*, and white poplar, *Populus alba*.

But most of Scotland is better suited, by soil and climate, to the growth of coniferous trees or softwoods, than to that of broadleaved trees or hardwoods. As soon as the lairds sought to extend their woods on to poorer ground, or farther up the hill, they favoured the hardy conifers. Already many foreign kinds had been grown in policies and gardens as curiosities. The Dukes of Argyll were growing European silver fir (*Abies alba*), Spanish fir (possibly *A. pinsapo*) and "pinaster", maritime pine from the Mediterranean (*Pinus maratima*), at Inveraray as early as 1685. The European larch, *Larix decidua*, was being grown by Alexander Brodie of Brodie, in Nairnshire, in 1656. Curiously, we do not know when the Norway spruce, *Picea abies*, was brought in, though it was being grown by the Duke of Argyll at Inveraray in 1682. The cedar of Lebanon, *Cedrus libani*, was planted by the Earl of Haddington before 1735; while the Weymouth pine, *Pinus strobus*, from North America, was being grown at Dunkeld by 1725.

Four of these new trees became really important as timber producers in Scotland—namely beech, sycamore, European larch, and Norway spruce. The first two are now thoroughly at home and spring up readily from self-sown seeds, but natural regeneration of larch and spruce is spasmodic and infrequent.

The explorations of the eighteenth and nineteenth centuries revealed a wealth of new trees native to the temperate regions of Asia and North America, that

PLATE 2   Norway spruce under snow.

could be grown in Scottish policies and gardens. The wealthier Scottish landowners vied with those of England in collecting rarities, and their arboreta, or collections of rare specimen trees, became as fine as any in Europe.

Scotsmen played the leading part in the discovery of the valuable conifers of western North America, from the growing of which the whole of the British Isles, and indeed all western Europe, has benefited. The first notable name is that of Archibald Menzies, botanist with Captain Vancouver's expedition to the Pacific in 1792. At Puget Sound in Alaska he discovered the Sitka spruce, destined to become the most widely planted tree in recent afforestation schemes; it was not introduced as a living tree, however, until David Douglas sent home seed in 1831. But Menzies did introduce to Britain the Californian redwood, *Sequoia sempervirens*, well known as the world's tallest tree, which is grown in Scotland solely for ornament. In 1795 Captain Vancouver's ship called at a Chilean port, where the dinner menu included the seeds of a curious conifer; Menzies pocketed a few, raised them on board ship, and so brought home that bizarre tree the monkey puzzle, *Araucaria araucana*.

David Douglas, the next great exploring Scottish botanist, was sent to British Columbia by the Horticultural Society of London at various times from 1823 to 1831. He sent home the seed of the magnificent conifer which preserves both his own name and that of Menzies, the Douglas fir, *Pseudotsuga menziesii*. He also introduced the Sitka spruce and the lodgepole pine, *Pinus contorta*, both now planted on a large scale in Scotland, besides two attractive silver firs, the noble fir, *Abies procera*, and the grand fir, *Abies grandis*.

In 1850 a group of Scottish landowners known as the Oregon Association was formed in Edinburgh to promote botanical collection in the Far West. Its collector, John Jeffrey, brought home the western hemlock, *Tsuga heterophylla*, an attractive and graceful conifer now widely planted in our woods. In 1854 an Edinburgh nurseryman named Lawson received from William Murray, another Scottish collector out in Oregon, the seed of the tree since universally known as Lawson cypress, *Chamaecyparis lawsoniana*, which has become a favourite for hedges and gardens.

To complete the tale of Scotland's forest trees, we must add the western red cedar, *Thuja plicata*, discovered in British Columbia by the Cornishman Lobb; the mighty wellingtonia, *Sequoiadendron giganteum*, found in California by the American John Bidwell, in 1841, but not introduced until 1853; and the Japanese larch, *Larix kaempferi*, imported by the Border nurseryman John Gould Veitch to his Exeter nurseries. This tree later became a parent of the Dunkeld Hybrid larch, *Larix eurolepis*, which first arose in Perthshire through chance cross breeding with the European larch.

The Growth of Scientific Forestry

William Boutcher, nurseryman at Comely Bank in Edinburgh, published in 1775 his *Treatise on Forest Trees*, which describes methods of raising, from seed or cuttings, a wide variety of kinds. J. C. Loudon, a Scottish botanist who settled in London, published in 1838 his *Arboretum et Fruticetum Brittanicum*, followed in 1842 by his *Trees and Shrubs*. These two books provide a conspectus of all the trees of the temperate zones known to science in his day. James Brown, a Victorian forester, wrote that praiseworthy though verbose manual *The Forester*, which became the standard guide for generations of practical men; it ran through six editions from 1847 to 1905. John Nisbet, who edited the later editions, is also noteworthy as a pioneer investigator of the history of Britain's forests.

Institutions concerned with the promotion of forestry flourished in Scotland at comparatively early dates, usually preceding those set up in England. The Royal Botanic Garden at Edinburgh was founded in 1680, eighty years before that at Kew. The Royal Scottish Forestry Society was founded (as the Scottish Arboricultural Society) in 1854, twenty-six years before its English counterpart. It draws its motto from a famous line from *The Heart of Midlothian*, written by Sir Walter Scott, himself a keen forester, in the Laird of Dumbiedyke's advice to his son:

"Jock, when ye hae naething else to do, ye may aye be sticking in a tree. It will be growing, while ye're sleeping."

Edinburgh University was the first in Britain to give systematic teaching in forestry; a lecturer was appointed in 1889.

The raising of young trees for sale as planting stock began in Scotland at an early date. One of the pioneers was Robert Dickson, who opened in 1729 a nursery at Hassendeanburn near Hawick. In 1754 he was selling "beach" and "plain" (sycamore) trees to "the Deuk of Queensberrie". In 1755 he opened a branch at Edinburgh, near Leith Walk, and his firm's business is still continued on the south side of that city. All the main nurseries in Scotland have been established along the east coast, where climate is favourable, soil fertile, and labour plentiful; they extend from Edinburgh north to Aberdeen, then west along the Moray Firth. For the past hundred years there has been a steady export of young trees to England. From the outset the Scottish nurserymen attached great importance to the right source of seed, naturally preferring the true indigenous strains.

At first all sawing of timber was done by hand; a pair of men called pit-sawyers moved a great saw up and down to cut through a log suspended over a pit, wherein the bottom sawyer sweated beneath a rain of sawdust. But crude sawmills operated by water or wind power were constructed early on; there was a water mill working at Rannoch about 1690, and another at Leith in 1695; a wind mill operating at Garmouth in Morayshire in 1786 drove no less than forty saws. The circular saw was introduced from England about 1820, and about this time steam power came to be used. Subsequently, about 1860, the "portable mill" was developed and became a characteristic feature of the Scottish woodland scene; it was powered by a great steam engine that could travel by road, and was so designed that it could be set up in a matter of days wherever logs were plentiful and be moved on when supplies ran out. Nowadays diesel power is usual in small woodland mills, while the equipment of large town mills is very elaborate and includes high speed band saws.

Scottish woods, nurseries and sawmills provided a training ground for young foresters, of whom a high proportion later sought posts in England or overseas. It was customary for a lad to train as an apprentice under a head forester, and at first that alone provided his recommendation to success. But as early as 1870 the Highland and Agricultural Society instituted an examination and a certificate in forestry; this was continued until 1935, when responsibility for this work was transferred to the Royal Scottish Forestry Society.

Twentieth Century Developments—Map: page 86

Simultaneously with the work of tree planting and the promotion of forest science, other forces were running their course which reduced the forests to a minor position in Scotland's economy. The natural woods had been neglected, and coppice working had become unprofitable. There had been imports of timber from Norway to Leith, for shipbuilding, as early as 1507, and with the Industrial Revolution of the nineteenth century imports reached so great a volume that they overshadowed home production. Though timber growing and harvesting never ceased, it came to be regarded as less and less essential; indeed, on some estates the woods were managed more for their sporting and landscape values than as sources of a key raw material. But all the time it was evident that the waste lands of Scotland had a great and unexploited capacity for timber growing. In 1907, the Office of Woods and Forests purchased the estate of Inverliever in Argyll, for a practical trial; 8,000 acres of plantations have since been established there, and are now yielding very substantial quantities of timber.

The need for large-scale action became apparent with the 1914–18 war, which showed how dependent Britain had become on overseas sources of timber—now an essential industrial material both in peace and war. In 1919 the Forestry Commission was established, under the chairmanship of Lord Lovat, as the appropriate national authority to carry out afforestation, and to encourage landowners to do likewise. The war of 1939–45 underlined the need for systematic forestry, for the huge fellings then found essential removed most of the timber stands spared in the previous conflict. Fortunately the plantations established since 1919 were still too young to suffer, and have survived as the nucleus of fresh woodland wealth.

An expanded programme of afforestation was set on foot in 1947. At the current rate of progress this will give Britain as a whole some 5 million acres of woodland by the end of the century, producing eventually about one fifth of her timber needs. Scotland's share in this new national forest estate will amount to more than half; and since, on a population basis, her consumption amounts to little more than one tenth of the total, she will shortly become self supporting in many classes of timber. By 1967, Scotland was able to meet all her needs of mining timber, cut largely from the smaller and younger trees, from her own woods. New sawmills, paper mills and board mills have already been set up to process logs from the new forests.

To summarise the work of the Forestry Commission in Scotland from 1919 to 1969, a period of fifty years, it had established 200 forests, spread over all the country except for the industrial regions and the most outlying islands. In 1967 it held, in round figures, 1,600,000 acres of ground, of which 1,000,000 was reckoned forest land, while the balance of 600,000 acres comprised, for the most part, mountainsides too high or infertile for tree growth. Woods and plantations covered 800,000 acres, while a further 200,000 acres awaited planting. This is proceeding at an average rate of 36,000 acres a year, involving about 60 million young trees annually. The number of forest workers and supervisors directly employed is in the region of 4,000, while another 1,000 engaged by timber merchants also find employment in the Commission's woods.

Five large forest regions have been declared Forest Parks. Modern mechanical methods of timber harvesting are progressing, and research work is in progress at numerous forests, forest nurseries and trial plots.

Private woodland owners are co-operating with the Commission on a large scale, mainly through the Dedication and Approved Woodlands schemes which embrace 400,000 acres; altogether they are planting some 15,000 acres of woodlands, and using about 30 million young trees, each year.

The Secretary of State for Scotland shares with the Minister of Agriculture, Fisheries and Food, and the Secretary of State for Wales, the responsibility for the general direction of Britain's forest policy; he has a particular concern for the Commission's operations in Scotland.

The harvesting of timber from the thinning out of the plantations increases yearly, both in volume and in value. In 1965, for example, 20,000 acres of the Forestry Commission's Scottish woods were thinned, and 10 million cubic feet of timber (hoppus measure) were harvested. This material was sold for £1,500,000. Much bigger returns are in prospect as more and more of the plantations reach the thinning stage. In a long-established and intensively managed forest estate of 1 million acres, such as Scotland will soon hold, 200,000 acres are normally thinned annually; production may therefore be expected to increase tenfold in the years to come. Private woodland owners currently market about 10 million cubic feet of timber each year. They are aiming at a major, though less marked, expansion of their timber harvest.

The traditional uses of timber in Scotland are for house building, shipbuilding, farm fencing, packaging of farm and fishery produce in every kind of box or container, as pit props in the mines and as railway sleepers and telegraph poles. These uses continue, but entirely new ones have been developed to meet modern needs. Paper making, using wood pulp from home-grown conifers, is the most striking development. The great new pulp and paper mill at Fort William, opened in 1966, represents an investment of £20 million in an entirely new industry for the Highlands, and will ultimately give employment to 1,000 people. Various kinds of man-made board, such as chipboard and hardboard, also use wood as their raw material. Modern factories to make these new products have been established at Annan in Dumfriesshire and Irvine in Ayrshire, while Scots-grown timber also flows to new factories in North-east England. Packaging board is made at Workington in Cumberland, and again the Scottish woods form a main source of raw material. The future, both for those who grow the trees and those who harvest the timber, is bright.

PLATE 3
Transplanting Sitka spruce trees for Scotland's future forests—a scene in a Border nursery. The boards, which are filled behind the windscreen, hold the rows of trees upright, at the right depth and distance apart.

2. Galloway Kirkcudbrightshire, Wigtownshire and Ayrshire

Map: page 46

The ancient province of Galloway, in the south-west of Scotland, remains a lovely yet lonely region where clear rivers run down from high moors to rich pastures fringing a coastline of rocky bays and golden sands. Three counties form a part of this delectable countryside, but here we shall ignore their boundaries and take first the incomparable southern strip along the Solway shore from Dumfries to Stranraer, and then turn inland to explore the remote wastes of heather, peat, and granite around Glen Trool and The Merrick.

The Southern Shore: Dumfries to Kirkcudbright

The coast road west from Dumfries winds past a low range of hills on which stands the young forest of Mabie, established since 1935, partly on former woodland and partly on heathy slopes. Its 5,700 acres of plantations include a wide variety of trees—Scots and Corsican pines, European and Japanese larches, Douglas fir, Norway and Sitka spruces, beech, ash and oak. Many of the woods have reached the thinning stage, for growth on this favoured southern edge of Scotland is rapid, and the harvesting of the small poles and logs provides steady work for local men.

A few miles farther west, the road runs through the estate of Shambellie, and passes, just opposite the lodge gate, the finest stand of Scots pine in all Scotland. It may seem odd to encounter this down in the south, for the pine is associated in most people's minds with the Highlands; but this magnificent tree is native here also, and there is a tradition that these splendid examples were raised from local seed. This estate has a continuous history of forest management for 200 years, some of its records dating back to 1752. These pines are known to have been planted in 1777, and are thus over 190 years old; they stand 100 feet tall, and average 100 stems to the acre. The stocking of timber is reckoned, in the forester's measure of hoppus cubic feet, at over 7,000 to the acre, an exceptional one for Scots pine anywhere in Europe.

The finest single pine has a girth of seven feet, and holds 120 hoppus feet of timber in its tall columnar stem. It is so shapely and vigorous that it has been selected by the Forestry Commission as a parent tree for propagating in seed orchards, to help found a new strain of Scots pines of proven worth. Interesting features of this stand are the trees' thick reddish bark, boldly patterned into a network of islands, and their very close spacing. It has been calculated that one small clump bears 18,000 hoppus feet, or 600 tons, to the acre!

A mile or so further on stands the romantic ruin of Sweetheart Abbey, so called because it was founded by the saintly Lady Devorguilla to hold the embalmed heart of her husband, John Balliol, who founded Balliol College at Oxford and whose family were contenders for the Scottish throne. The abbey, built of local red sandstone, once housed a community of Cistercian monks whose sheep roamed the neighbouring hills, to the detriment of their forest cover.

Next the road rounds the slopes of that grand summit Criffel, which rises to 1,866 feet and commands all the Solway; here the climate is so mild that the Ayrshire cattle can graze out of doors long into the winter. For several miles the road follows a shelf on the hillside, affording wonderful views over the wide firth towards the peaks of the English Lake District. Soon we reach Dalbeattie Forest, which extends for four miles, from the coast around Rockcliffe and Kippford to the grey granite town of Dalbeattie. Together with outlying portions, this forest extends to 6,300 acres, or nearly ten square miles, and provides a form of scenic beauty rare in southern Scotland—woodland running down to sheltered inlets. Here, beside the estuary of the Urr Water or by the sands of Southwick Bay, you may encounter pines, larches, and spruces clothing the slopes; and hear the whine of the saw as the foresters thin out their thriving crops. Here too the naturalist may find a wealth of bird life, from the wildfowl of the Solway mudflats to the goldcrests of the pinewoods.

Kirkcudbright and Gatehouse of Fleet

Continuing westward, we pass the green larchwoods of the Munches Estate and the sawmills of Palnackie, a tiny seaport on the banks of the Urr Water, and then travel below the outlying sections of Dalbeattie Forests on the slopes of Bengairn Hill. Munches, by the way, holds Scotland's stoutest known Scots pine, a tree thirteen feet in girth. At length we reach Kirkcudbright, a dreamtown of white-walled houses set in a curve of the estuary of the Galloway Dee; a place sparklingly clean and tidy, its bustling days as a seaport all but forgotten, now a haunt of artists and lovers of the picturesque. Much of the beauty of its surroundings comes from the fringes of broadleaved trees—oak, ash, beech, and sycamore, that line the Dee, both along its upper reaches and out seawards towards Kirkcudbright Bay. Many of these form a part of the woods and policies of the estate of St. Mary's Isle, which takes its name from the peninsula south of the town.

Continue westwards for eight miles or so, and you come to the tiny tidy township of Gatehouse of Fleet. Like all the towns in Galloway, it seems too imposing for its purely rural surroundings; further exploration will reveal that, as a rule, there is too much uncultivated moorland and too little good farmland around each of them to give them much standing as market towns. At Gatehouse, however, forestry provides a useful source of employment, for just to the south of the town, in the grounds around Cally Palace, which is now a hotel, there is a nursery of nearly fifty acres, which requires a strong squad to tend its millions of tiny trees. The plantations of Fleet Forest, which surrounds the nursery, have mostly been formed on old woodland sites, having a fertile soil and being blessed with a particularly mild maritime climate. Consequently broadleaved trees have been used to make up much of their 2,800 acres. The main kinds planted are oak, ash, beech, sycamore, alder, and birch; European larch is used to nurse them up through their early stages.

PLATE 4
Loch Ken and the wooded slopes of Cairn Edward, Bennan Forest, South of New Galloway, Kirkcudbrightshire.

Newton Stewart and the Machers of Wigtown

Beyond Gatehouse the road skirts the tree-lined shores of the shallow estuary of the Water of Fleet, passing the ruin of Cardoness Castle and giving fascinating views over the three little Islands of Fleet on the fringe of Wigtown Bay. Two further ruined keeps are passed as the highway swings round within view of the wide sands, or rather mudflats, that line the estuary of the River Cree. Beyond the village of Creetown we meet the broad marshland pastures through which the Cree winds in a tortuous course, and near Palnure pass below Kirroughtree Forest, a portion of the Glen Trool Forest Park to which we shall presently return. Newton Stewart, where the Cree is crossed, is another of the surprisingly clean and neat Galloway townships. It lies just within Wigtownshire, but its eastern portion, called Minnigaff, stands in Kirkcudbrightshire, and both share the prosperity brought by a textile mill and a large sawmill that consumes locally grown timber.

South-west of Newton Stewart lies the lonely, little-visited peninsula called the Machers (or moorlands) of Wigtown, holding the towns of Wigtown and Whithorn with two or three features of forestry interest. Four miles south of Wigtown stands the forest of Kilsture, covering 2,700 acres in all. Here 500 acres of broadleaved woodland—chiefly oak, ash, and beech, have been established on former woodland soil. A few miles to the south-east, around Garliestown, there are extensive belts of beech and other hardwoods around the fertile fields that neighbour Galloway House.

Over on the west coast lies the estate of Monreith, the seat of the Maxwell family. The late Sir Herbert Maxwell was widely known as a charming writer who did much to make known the antiquities of Scotland and to ensure their preservation; he was also a keen arboriculturist, and planted here many trees rare in Scotland and barely hardy except in the south-west. He grew, for example, specimens of Californian trees like the Monterey pine (*Pinus radiata*), the Monterey cypress (*Cupressus macrocarpa*), and the western white pine (*Pinus monticola*). Most of the woodlands naturally carry the commoner kinds of trees, both coniferous and broadleaved, but there is one plantation that is believed to be unique in Britain. This consists of the common Monkey Puzzle Tree, or Chile Pine, *Araucaria araucana*, which is often seen as a garden specimen, though scarcely ever in plantations, despite the facts that it has a good timber and forms vast forests in its native Andes. There are two acres of these rather bizarre trees, which number over 700 individuals. They were planted about 1910, and by 1956 the tallest specimens had reached a height of thirty-six feet, while many stems had a girth of two feet. However, these rates of growth and timber production are not impressive, and the most remarkable feature of this plantation is the way it has stood up to fierce gales

sweeping over the open Irish Sea, immediately south-west.

Going north-west, towards the neck of that curious hammerhead peninsula that ends in the Mull of Galloway, the country becomes moorland in character, and it is on these moors that the bulk of the new forest called Bareagle has been established. Its 4,800 acres include an expanse of uplands two miles north-west of Glenluce, and also a few outliers; and on these areas Sitka spruce and lodgepole pine figure largely in the planting. But another portion of Bareagle Forest has a very different situation, for it extends in a narrow strip along the Luce Sands, at the head of Luce Bay. These were moving sand-dunes, liable at any time to drift inland before the wind and to engulf fertile fields; now they have been fixed in place by the establishment of Corsican pines, hardy trees that tolerate dry and sterile soils provided the climate is warm and sunny. Bareagle Forest also includes a big forest nursery, covering sixty acres, which is situated immediately south of the old Dunragit Station. This big nursery was started in 1950 in order to take advantage of the readily worked sandy soil in a region of low rainfall; it draws its labour force, which includes a large proportion of women and girls, from the Stranraer and Glenluce districts.

Stranraer and the Mull of Galloway

Between Glenluce and Stranraer the main road runs through the extensive woodlands of the Lochinch Estate, owned by the Earl of Stair. Particular success has been obtained with the Japanese larch, which appears to find the mild maritime climate much to its liking, for it grows remarkably fast; the oldest wood, planted in 1899, still had 133 trees to the acre at the age of fifty years, with a volume of 6,000 hoppus feet, remarkably high for a tree reputed to give only moderate volumes of timber.

The narrow peninsula beyond Stranraer, called the Rhinns of Galloway, facing Ireland only twenty miles away across the North Channel, has a fair sprinkling of woodland. In the north there are plantations around Lochnaw Castle, and in the centre a small Commission plantation east of Portpatrick. Away to the south, near the Mull of Galloway, famous as the meeting place of the seven tides that sweep these turbulent seas, lies the estate of Logan. It holds numerous woodlands and fine decorative gardens wherein such sub-tropical trees as palms and dracaenas (*Cordyline australis*) are grown. For this is, perhaps, the mildest and least frosty corner of Scotland.

Up the Galloway Dee towards the Rhinns of Kells

From such sub-tropical scenes we turn inland to the real heart of Galloway. Go north from any point in its fertile, pastoral, coastal fringe, and you will be surprised to find how soon the moors and mosses encompass you around. Here stand the highest hills, the remotest lochs, and the loneliest countryside in the South of Scotland. Here you can walk, if you wish, into glens devoid of any dwelling, and find yourself five miles or more from the merest semblance of a road or cart track. And here you may encounter herds of wild red deer or, more surprisingly, herds of shaggy-coated, long-horned, wild goats. Except when the mists lower on the fells, this is colourful country too; it was the late Andrew McCormick, the Galloway author who roamed the highest peaks from his home at Newton Stewart long after his eightieth birthday, who first opened the eyes of many visitors to its rich hues and patterns. The rivers of Galloway, he said, run like streams of molten silver down to sands of burnished gold. You can add to these the purple of the heather, the russet of the fading bracken, and the soft tints of pink and grey on the boulders of weathered granite, the deep brown of exposed peat, and the rich crimson that stains the heart of the pale green tussocks of sphagnum moss. Remember too that all the everyday colours of milder landscapes are here also—the varied greens of well-grazed pastures, oakwoods, and spruce plantations, and the black of the rich marshland soil newly turned by the plough; add the whiteness of the harled farmhouses with their grey slated roofs, and the picturesque black-and-white belted Galloway cattle, and you have a rare blending of contrast and harmony.

Galloway—the land of the Gael—off the main tracks of Scottish history yet closely interwoven with it. A land that has lost its language, for although the Gaelic tongue lingered here until a few centuries ago, not a proverb, scarcely a legend, survives on the lips of the people. Yet the place-names are nearly all plainly of Gaelic derivation, Anglicised in spelling though most have become; and though opinions differ as to the original meaning of each, it is clearly good Scots Gaelic, with hardly a hint of Welsh in its make-up. The few intrusive words are Norse, and they linger mostly along the coast, where a hill may be called a *fell*, a harbour a *fleet*, and a headland a *ness*.

The historic associations of Galloway are largely with Robert the Bruce, who fought several minor campaigns against the English in its wild rock fastnesses before he emerged as Scotland's national leader. Also, with the Covenanters who met in fearful prayer meetings amid the hills, being persecuted for their faith by the established Scottish government of King Charles II. At one time the region was famous for its small sturdy horses, but their breed is now extinct. The name of "Galloway" is more commonly applied to two breeds of hornless beef cattle, one plain and the other boldly belted with white, which both show exceptional hardihood and the ability to thrive on poor moorland pastures. It is also famed for its wool, of the coarse type yielded by hardy blackface sheep; and it will soon become famous for its forests.

Hydro-electric Power

The eastern frontier of these Galloway highlands may be taken as the River Dee, which is the life-blood of one of the earliest hydro-electric schemes in Scotland, now controlled by the South Scotland Electricity Board. The huge volume of water that flows into it and its tributary streams, and also into Loch Doon faraway in Ayrshire, has been cunningly exploited to give the maximum power, sometimes from fairly small descents. There is a big barrage and power station at Tongland, a few miles above the Dee's estuary at Kirkcudbright; and another dam at Glenlochar, three miles north-west of the neat white-walled town of Castle Douglas. The purpose of this higher dam is to hold a constant supply of water in Loch Ken, the name applied to a long, still stretch of the Dee's course, which extends for twelve miles north-west to the wee township of New Galloway. North of that point the land becomes higher, and a series of dams and power stations exploits the rapid fall of the Dee. Its waters are augmented by a tunnel that "captures" Loch Doon, diverting southwards most of the stream that would otherwise flow north to the town of Ayr. Loch Doon has been deepened by the building of a couple of dams, while the headwaters of the Dee itself are also impounded in the artificial Clatteringshaws Loch, west of New Galloway, to secure a more suitable fall.

Within the curve formed by the Dee—between Kirkcudbright and the Southern end of Loch Ken, lie the well-wooded estates of Balmaghie and Hensol, and two Commission forests. Laurieston, the older of these, rises majestically from the shores of Woodhall Loch up the slopes of Craigelwhan and Kennich Hill; it extends to 5,500 acres, and its thriving plantations are mostly of spruces, larches and pines; planting began here in 1939. Adjoining Laurieston to the south, around Loch Whinyeon and the hill of Bengray, is the younger forest of Glengap, situated amid lonely, peaty moors that run down towards Gatehouse. Glengap holds 2,200 acres, and its planting, mainly with Norway and Sitka spruces, was begun in 1948.

Bennan Forest and Loch Ken—*Plate 4*

South of New Galloway town, a five-mile stretch of Loch Ken has been beautified by the extensive plantations of the Bennan Forest, which run right over the summit of Cairn Edward hill, 1,066 feet above sea level, and extend to about 14,500 acres. These magnificent woods along the western shore of the loch consist of Douglas fir, Norway and Sitka spruces, Scots pine, and European and Japanese larches, whose outlines and varied hues combine to give a rich tapestry of form and colour clothing the long slope. A fringe of alders along the water's edge, and the expanse of still water, often studded with wildfowl, complete a grand picture. Yet the forest element of this landscape is comparatively recent, for planting did not begin here until 1922; growth was rapid, and twenty-five years later the first thinnings were yielding pitwood, fencing material, and small saw timber, while a network of roads was being built to enable this material to be hauled out. The rapid increase in employment, to a figure around seventy men, had made it necessary to build two groups of new houses beside New Galloway—a welcome development for a tiny burgh where life ran slowly.

In the heart of Bennan Forest there stands one of the pathetic Martyr's Monuments that commemorate pious Covenanters who died for their faith. It records that Robert Fergusson, J. McMichan, R. Stuart and J. Grier were surprised and slain by Graham of Claverhouse on 18th December, 1684.

Clatteringshaws and the Rhinns of Kells—*Plate 8*

To the north-west of Clatteringshaws Loch stands the neighbouring forest called The Garraries, occupying 10,000 acres of land between the headwaters of the Dee and that grand range of hills called the Rhinns of Kells. It runs up to their highest peak, Corserine, 2,658 feet above sea level, but although much of it is so high-lying, half of it is destined for planting up with spruces and pines. A road has been run in to it from Clatteringshaws, so ending the amazing isolation typified by the story of the Backhill of the Bush, a shepherd's cottage long since deserted. The story goes that when the shepherd there married a wife, he took her over the hills on pony back; and there for five long years she remained, never emerging by the hill track, and seeing nobody save her husband, who brought in all their supplies.

Going north up the main valley from New Galloway, beside the stream that is no longer called the Dee but the Water of Ken, one encounters an impressive succession of power stations, dams, lochs, and surge towers. Away to the west, towards the majestic Rhinns of Kells and the grimly named Loch Dungeon, extends the huge estate called The Forrest. This is now the scene of one of the largest private ventures in afforestation in Scotland; it was sponsored by a Norwegian concern and includes several thousand acres of coniferous plantations. On either side of the long Kendoon Loch, below the high road, there may be seen the green spruces of Dundeugh Forest, which look surprisingly mature although none of the woods was planted before 1936. This forest now extends for six miles to the west, in fact right to the summit ridge of the Rhinns of Kells, and embraces 5,000 acres. Beyond Dundeugh the road to Ayr winds on through the treeless uplands around Carsphairn, below the lofty summit of Cairnsmore of

Carsphairn, which at 2,612 feet is the highest of the three Cairnsmores or "great mountains"—the others are Dee and Fleet—for which Galloway is famous.

To the east of New Galloway the forest of Garcrogo, 3,000 acres, follows the typical pattern of spruce plantations, with some larches and pines, established on ploughed ground. A cairn in the Corriedoo section, at the northern end of this forest, is said to mark the spot where the last wild boar in all Scotland was killed; but the date of this memorable event has not been recorded.

New Galloway to Newton Stewart

The main road south-west from New Galloway, towards Newton Stewart, reveals a wild aspect of these south-western forests, for it traverses lonely moorlands around the lofty Cairnsmore of Dee, over 2,000 feet above sea level, which are only gradually being brought under tree crops; indeed, the granite-strewn summits lie too high to attract the tree planter. In this Clatteringshaws Forest of some 14,000 acres, Sitka spruce and lodgepole pine are the main trees planted, for they are tolerant to the poor peaty soil and resistant to the considerable exposure. The new woods extend up the course of the Dee, as well as along the highway, and some lie on the western side of Clatteringshaws Loch. Just beside this impressive, though purely artificial sheet of water, on its eastern shore, is the battlefield of Rapploch Moss, where Bruce overcame an English force in 1307; the stone where the king stood that day may still be seen, and it now bears the inscription:

" The Bruce's Stone.
Upon this Moss Raploch
Robert the Bruce
Earl of Carrick, Lord of the Garrioch,
Defeated the English in 1307"

Up the Cree to Glen Trool—*Title page picture*

Our next exploration into the wilds of the Galloway highlands starts at Newton Stewart, nestling so peacefully beside its bridge and weir across the lower reach of the River Cree. First let us look at Kirroughtree Forest which neighbours it on the east. This is best seen from the high road to New Galloway, which strikes its plantations a mile or so from the town, and is then bordered by tall Japanese larches for another five miles; vigorous trees these, distinguished by russet twigs in winter and bluish green foliage through the summer months. This portion of the forest ends in rocky heights, planted with hardy Scots pines, near the point where a stone obelisk recalls a local linguist, Professor Murray, and a sparkling burn plunges down from the west by two cataracts, each called "The Grey Mare's Tail". Away to the west another arm of the forest, where thousands of spruces are being planted, runs far up the Penkiln Burn towards the summit of Lamachan Hill, above Glen Trool. To the south, a forest road winds down Bargaly Glen to

Palnure, passing on the way a forest nursery covering sixty acres, where millions of tiny trees are raised from seed. Much of the work of seed sowing, transplanting, and weeding is done by women and girls. Altogether Kirroughtree Forest employs nearly one hundred people on its 13,000 acres. The earliest plantations were made in 1930, and these reached the thinning stage in 1955.

If you take the Girvan road that runs north-west from Newton Stewart, you will have as your companion for seven miles the babbling river Cree, flowing down from the wild hills that form the Range of the Awful Hand. Its banks are fringed with alders, and there is a sprinkling of old oakwoods on the eastern, or Kirkcudbrightshire, side. Four miles out from Newton Stewart you pass, on the western or Wigtownshire bank, the young forest called Penninghame, which includes 9,000 acres of peaty moorlands, undergoing afforestation with

Norway and Sitka spruces. Three miles farther on, at the hamlet of Bargrennan, the road forks, and if you leave the high road and take the right-hand route, you will come, in less than a mile, upon one of the surprises of the forests of Scotland. For here, in the heart of lonely hills and peat mosses, stands the entirely new village called Glentrool, built as recently as 1953 to house the workers in the Glen Trool Forest Park. Its lay-out allows for some fifty houses, implying a population of some 200 to 250 people, and although construction is not yet complete there are already so many children living here that it has been found necessary to build a new school.

Not many years ago you could have motored up the valley of the River Minnoch and seen only tiny farmsteads, spaced far apart and providing a scant livelihood for only a handful of sheep graziers; at Rowantree stood

PLATE 5
Looking westwards over Loch Trool, in the heart of Glen Trool Forest, Kirkcudbrightshire.

Natural woods of the native Sessile oak, *Quercus petraea*, below Buchan Hill at the head of Loch Trool, Glen Trool Forest Park, Kirkcudbrightshire.

a tiny schoolhouse, with chickens perched on its window-sills, undeterred by the lessons in progress a few feet away. Now all this has been changed by the planting up of the largest forest group in the south-west. The big tractor-drawn ploughs have scarred and drained the peaty wastes, and the spruces and pines are springing up in their trim ranks as far as the eye can see. In the Glen Trool Forest alone there are nearly 52,000 acres of land, of which 25,000 had been put under trees by 1967; 3,000 more are scheduled for future planting, while the remaining 26,000 acres form a high wilderness of rock and peak, much of which can never be satisfactorily afforested. The land was acquired from the Earl of Galloway in 1939, and planting began in 1945.

Loch Trool—*Plates 5 and 6*

For the visitor the main attraction is the Glen of Trool itself, which is easily found by taking another right-handed turn just beyond the village. After crossing the Minnoch the foot of the great Merrick range is reached, and the country suddenly takes on a truly Highland aspect. Within a few miles the road swings out on a narrow bank above lovely Loch Trool, aptly called in Gaelic, *loch t-sruthail*, or "the rivershaped loch", that winds for a mile and a half into the hills. The road ends at the Bruce's Stone, a modern memorial commanding a glorious view. Here, so tradition maintains, stood Robert the Bruce on that fateful day in 1306, when he routed an English force sent to capture him in this distant fastness. Forewarned of their coming, he slipped over to the northern side of the loch, leaving his men to set an ambush on the southern shore. The English had to pass along that narrow ledge, which you can still see from this spot, called the Steps o' Trool, and when they reached it Bruce blew a blast upon his hunting horn, as a signal to his men on the far cliffs. Great stones were promptly rolled down the precipices, to slay many English yeomen and throw the rest into confusion, before the Scots charged down the braes to complete their defeat.

At the lower, western end of the loch, close to Caldon's Farm, there is a public camping ground, delightfully situated amid woods of hazel and oak. Within a few

PLATE 7   Scots pine and silver birch beside Loch Doon. The road leads to Starr Forest, on the Ayrshire side of the Glen Trool Forest Park, and the far hill is Craiglee.

PLATE 8
The Rhinns of Kells, Kirkcudbrightshire: Black Craig, Portmark, Meaul and far Corserine. Seen across Loch Doon in the Glen Trool Forest Park.

hundred yards of this stands one of the most stirring memorials to the Covenanters' stand for religious freedom. Let the quaintly graven contemporary inscription tell its sufficient tale:

Here lyes James and Robert Duns, Thomas and John Stevensons, James McClive, Andreu McCall, who were surprised at prayer, in this house, by Colonel Douglas, Lieutnant Livingston, Cornet James Douglas, and by them most impiously and cruelly murthered for their adherence to Scotland's Reformation Covenants National and Solemn League 1685."

The Merrick Wilderness

From the Bruce's Stone there is an easy, grassy, ascent up the Buchan Burn to the summit of The Merrick, which with its 2,764 feet stands the highest summit of the Southern Uplands. A surprising number of rounded hilltops—cairns, laws, and fells, in that vast rolling sea of hills which stretches eastwards to the Cheviots, closely approach it in elevation. To the east the view is limited by its rivals the Rhinns of Kells, but westwards the eye can range far over Ayrshire to the Firth of Clyde; southwest lie Wigtownshire and Ireland, while to the south the peaks of the Isle of Man are sometimes in view.

Yet the eye of the hill wanderer is more likely to be held by the strange wilderness of granite, lochan and peat bog that lies at the back of the summit, hidden away unsuspected. Crockett, the Galloway author, called it "a weird, wild world, new and strange, not yet out of chaos, not yet approved of God", and it has also been aptly termed "the riddlin's o' creation". In reality it is the aftermath of the great glaciers that scoured these hills, leaving hollows in the rocks, striations on their smooth surfaces, and moraines of gravel over which clear waters course to tumble over sparkling waterfalls. Try—in fair weather—a little exploration of these wastes of hard granite and spongy peat, and you will realise the truth of the local saying: "It taks a *man* to herd The Merrick".

Yet for the hardy hiker there are rewards in this stern fastness: the "Loch-in-Loch", a tiny lochan on an islet in Loch Enoch, unique in Scotland; a "Murder Hole", fringed with rushes, in a deep peaty pool; a beach of gleaming silver sand; an outlaw's hiding hole; and a vast peat bog called the Silver Flow that has been adopted by the Nature Conservancy as a classic of its kind. The name of "The Merrick" stems from *tiugh meuraich*, Gaelic for "the sturdy finger", for as seen from the north-west the summit forms the highest knuckle of a gigantic "hand" of parallel peaks.

Loch Doon—*Plate 7*

Glen Trool Forest extends over the Ayrshire boundary, where it adjoins the big forest group of Tairlaw, the Starr and Changue, all within the Glen Trool Forest Park. Changue, which rises from the peaceful village of Barr to the grassy Polmaddie Hills, covers 3,000 acres, largely under spruce, all planted since 1936. Tairlaw and the Starr, which reach for twelve miles from the River Stinchar to Loch Doon, near Dalmellington, were acquired from the Cassilis Estates in 1945 and hold 33,500 acres; but so highlying, wild, rocky, and peaty are these uplands that only 15,000 acres of this is currently considered suitable for afforestation; spruces and the hardy lodgepole pine are the main trees used. There is a profusion of burns, lochs, and lochans, some holding numbers of big brown trout, scattered over the rainswept moorlands of the upper reaches. Loch Doon, now a reservoir, has on its shores the re-erected ruins of a mediaeval castle which, before the water level was raised, stood on a rocky islet in its midst. Altogether the Park holds nearly 130,000 acres of the wildest and most romantic scenery of the south-west; it is in fact the biggest Forest Park in Britain.

There is one further forest in these Galloway moors, that called Arecleoch, which occupies 4,200 acres in the roadless, peaty waste between Glen App and the railway line from Glasgow to Stranraer.

In the south-west of Ayrshire there is a fair sprinkling of woodland on private estates around Ballantrae, Barrhill, and Pinmore, giving a sylvan aspect to the brown hills that hem in the lower course of the River Stinchar.

Central and Northern Ayrshire—*Plate 9*

Leaving the wild heights of Galloway for the bowl of rich pasture lands that encircles the town of Ayr, we reach the lower valley of the Water of Girvan, which is thickly clothed in tall trees. Six miles inland from Girvan town stands Kilgrammie Forest, where the Commission is raising plantations of oak, beech and Norway spruce on 600 acres of former woodland and moorland acquired in 1949.

Higher up the valley are the extensive woodlands of the Blairquhan Estate, where Sir James Hunter Blair has carried out notable experiments in the establishment of new timber trees. He has had particular success with a fine strain of European larch brought in as seed from Krzyskich in Poland, and he has also raised a good stand of the American larch or tamarack, *Larix laricina*, on a patch of deep peat. His woods cover 700 acres, and include a large proportion of broadleaved trees—oak, ash, beech and sycamore, which here regenerate themselves readily from naturally fallen seed. Natural seedlings of the European silver fir and the western hemlock are also frequent. Hence it is possible to manage many of the woods on what is called a Group Selection System; this means that as the timber matures small groups of the older trees are felled; the natural regrowth of seedlings, supplied and sheltered by the surrounding trees, gradually fills the gaps; and then the fellings are extended in stages until the whole wood has been replenished. This saves the cost of replanting, and preserves a permanent and attractive woodland cover.

Culzean Castle, on the coast between Girvan and Ayr, is well known as one of the larger properties of the Scottish National Trust, and is open to visitors; it also forms the Scottish residence of General Eisenhower. On the adjoining Culzean Estate the Earl of Stair maintains several hundred acres of woods, managed on scientific lines, together with a sawmill, a creosoting plant, and a forest nursery for raising young trees.

Inland from Ayr towards Cumnock and Kilmarnock, and even far up the River Ayr towards Sorn, there is a fair sprinkling of woodland that represents the efforts of the big landowners, during the eighteenth and nineteenth centuries, to establish amenity woods and game preserves around their mansion houses, and shelter-belts on the verge of the hill ground. Beech and sycamore featured largely in these plantations; they were frequently planted with the aid of Scots pine or larch as nurse trees; but as a rule the nurses, maturing earlier, have already been harvested, and only the broadleaved trees survive. On exposed ridges they are often contorted by the fierce, salt-laden south-westerly gales, blowing off the Firth of Clyde, into windswept outlines that suggest they are leaning over to one side. But this very distortion serves as a measure of their value as a shield to crops and livestock alike. Along the coast near Ardrossan and West Kilbride this wind-moulding is most pronounced, but it also extends well inland, being evident around Mauchline on land at 500 feet elevation and ten miles from the sea.

An interesting application of forestry as an aid to industry is found at the big Imperial Chemical Industries explosives factory at Stevenston near Saltcoats. Here the installations are scattered among sand dunes as a safety measure, each being isolated by earth banks to limit the spread of shock should an explosion occur. But the sand drifted with the wind and was liable to fill the hollows and block the roadways. Therefore trees were planted as windscreens, for as soon as the velocity of the wind is checked it loses its power to transport sand grains, and the dunes become, in fact, fixed. The tree selected for this arduous task was the Corsican pine, which thrives on dry sand and withstands salt-laden winds.

A number of forest industries are centred on Ayrshire, and though some are only on a small scale they illustrate the value of timber to varied aspects of Scotland's economy. The little port of Troon has sawmills and timber yards that deal extensively in softwoods—redwood from the pines and whitewood from the spruces, imported from Europe and North America. It is also the home of a big sawmilling firm that handles large quantities of Scottish-grown timbers, of all kinds; and maintains nurseries to further the replanting of felled woods. The whisky blenders at Kilmarnock use oak for barrels, and softwoods for packing cases; while the foundries in the same town use a great deal of timber—

including much Scots pine—to make the patterns for their metal castings. There is also a chipboard factory at Irvine.

Two new forests have recently been established by the Commission on high hill ground in mid-Ayrshire. Kyle, north of Dalmellington, covers 2,300 acres, while Whitelee, north-west of Kilmarnock, occupies 2,100. Spruces play a leading part in all these new plantations.

PLATE 9
A long straight road across the Ayrshire uplands, close to Mauchline; the crowns of the sheltering beeches have been moulded by the south-west gales.

PLATE 10   Pony-trekkers on a forest road through the Aberfoyle larchwoods.   Queen Elizabeth Forest Park.

3. From Clyde to Forth

Lanark, Renfrew, Dunbarton, Stirling and South-West Perthshire

Maps: pages 45 and 46

Lanarkshire and Clydesdale—*Plates 11 and 45*

The large county of Lanark holds virtually the whole basin of the great River Clyde, from its source amid the wide green spaces of the Lowther Hills, down to the very heart of the busy city of Glasgow, where it first bears seagoing vessels on its broad stream. The starting point of this great river is often held to be at the head of the Little Clyde, near Elvanfoot, where the main road from Glasgow to Carlisle begins its final climb across the wild uplands, over into Annandale.

But to find the remotest source of the Clyde waters, at the head of their longest stream, you must rove through a roadless wilderness of high sheep pastures for a further ten miles south, in fact over into Dumfriesshire and to the top of Queensberry, 2,285 feet above sea level. There lies the origin of the longest tributary of the Daer Water, largest of the upper headwaters of the Clyde. This joins another stream called the Potrail Water, at a point poetically called Watermeetings. That name has been chosen for a new forest, around the one thousand foot level, which is to comprise 2,000 acres of plantations. It lies close to the high road, which follows the Potrail Water before descending through the steep defile of the Dalveen Pass on its way south to Dumfries.

The Potrail Water joins the Little Clyde near Elvanfoot, so named because there a third stream, the Elvan Water, comes down from the west. Near its headwaters stands Leadhills, famous as the highest village in Scotland, standing 1,400 feet above the sea. Once Leadhills had thriving lead mines, and there is a local tradition that much of the oak of Nithsdale and upper Clydesdale was cleared to provide supports for the underground workings, or charcoal for the smelting of the ores. But the landscape of this region today is surprisingly treeless, a vast waste of hills, over which the winds sweep and sough unceasingly, the haunt of whaup and sandpiper, with its grass everywhere cropped short by the blackface sheep. The main interest of tree planters along the upper Clyde has been with shelter, sometimes to shield isolated farmsteads with sycamore, and sometimes to protect the lower in-by fields with belts of pines, so that sheep may find safe havens from winter blizzards.

To the east of the village of Crawford, up the stream called the Camps Water, several hundred acres of young plantations, largely of spruce, have been established by a Water Board on its gathering grounds. Abington, a few miles farther down the Clyde, has a group of shelter woods, and at that point the main Glasgow road leaves the river for a score of miles, striking north-west over the hills direct to Hamilton. On its way it crosses the valley of the Douglas Water, near the estate of Douglas Castle, which holds a large group of woodlands, spread in a circular fashion to enclose its better lands.

The railway and an alternative road take the easier course down the river, passing through Symington to the east of the Tinto Hills; they enter a broad bowl amid the uplands, through which the Clyde follows a tortuous course, making countless lesser loops in three great semicircular swerves—first east towards Biggar, then north to Carstairs, and finally south below Lanark. The floor of the dale lies 600 feet above sea level, and being surrounded by thousand-foot hills and far removed from the tempering influence of the sea, it suffers a severe winter climate. The proprietors of the several great estates realised, two centuries ago, that their lands were marginal for agriculture, which could only flourish where shelter was provided, and so they built up the finest system of planned shelterbelts in Scotland. Some of these have since suffered neglect, but this important aspect of tree growing is again receiving the attention it deserves. Researches at the University of Edinburgh have confirmed, for Scottish conditions, what was already becoming widely known abroad— that well-conceived belts of trees, on level land, will provide appreciable shelter for a distance equal to twenty times their own height. Increases in the yields from crops and stock amply compensate for the loss of the land that supports the trees.

To illustrate the importance of these belts in the local economy, we may take the estate of Lee and Carnwath, which lie between the Clyde and the Pentlands. This includes 220 acres managed as shelterbelts, together with some 800 acres that are run with timber production as the main objective. Several of the larger woods on this estate are managed on a selection system, whereby they need never be clear-felled and replanted. Instead, individual trees are selected for removal as they become mature, in such a way that the gaps they leave will be filled in by natural regrowth of young seedling trees. So the forest cover need never be removed, and young saplings will always benefit from the shelter of older trees—for on open ground in this region young trees often suffer setbacks from frost, wind, and drought. This selection method works well, and in fact is often seen at its best, where several kinds of trees are grown in mixture, each exploiting both the ground and air space in its own particular way. As an example, the West Wood on the Lee estate holds nine sorts of timber trees growing harmoniously together; these are: sycamore, ash, beech, wych elm, oak, gean or wild cherry, European larch, European silver fir, and Norway spruce.

Clydesdale Forest is the name given to a group of several scattered woodlands, around Lanark and Carstairs, covering 2,000 acres, which the Forestry Commission has planted since 1953. These include some beautiful stretches of the river bank close to the famous waterfalls at Corra Linn and Bonnington Linn. Clydesdale is a district noted for its orchards, but one has only to travel a few miles to the north to encounter bare peaty moors where the growing of any sort of crop—whether by farmer or forester—becomes something of an achievement. Such an area is the Couthalley Bog, north of Carstairs, where improvement for grazing has proved

PLATE II
A bull, a calf and a cow of the Cadzow herd of wild white cattle. Cadzow Park, near Hamilton, Lanarkshire, holds fine old oaks, birches and ash trees surviving from the ancient Clydesdale Forests.

PLATE 12
The shapely cone of Ben Lomond, in the Queen Elizabeth Forest Park, Stirlingshire; seen from the western shore of Loch Lomond close to Tarbet.

impracticable; the peat has now been ploughed and drained by the Commission, which is using its hardiest available trees—the native Scots pine, and the lodgepole pine and Sitka spruce from British Columbia—to see how far timber growing is practicable on the bleak wastes of Central Scotland.

Below Lanark, coal mines and ironworks begin to encroach upon the green dale of the Clyde, which here runs through a deep, narrow cleft in the broad tableland of moors and hill pastures. Yet a fair sprinkling of woodland survives the increasing industrialisation. South of Hamilton, near Cadzow Castle, the seat of the Duke of Hamilton, part of the ancient Cadzow Forest still remains. Cadzow was an oak wood, and a well-known picture of timber hauling in its midst, painted about the year 1800, reveals the open character to which it had been reduced, partly by felling and partly

by the continual grazing of sheep, cattle and ponies. The grand veteran trees, gnarled and branchy, are at least the equals of those that grew in the English Forests of Windsor, and Dean, or the New Forest, under kinder conditions much farther south. As in England, these oaks were prized for shipbuilding, being sent down the Clyde to the shipyards of Dumbarton. Cadzow is famous as the home of a herd of wild white cattle, with black ears, feet and muzzles, which has survived like its oaks from the remote past, when many herds roamed the woods of Caledon.

Glasgow

Closer in to Glasgow one would hardly expect trees to survive the smoky atmosphere, together with the fumes from heavy industries, yet on the fringes of the city there are two notable woodlands. One is at Nether

25

Pollok to the south-west, where extensive woods are preserved by the National Trust; the other is at Garscube on the north-west, where Glasgow University has acquired an estate, once owned by Sir Archibald Campbell, which includes a large arboretum or collection of specimen trees. The Glasgow Botanical Gardens are situated in a notably smoky district, but there, and even lower down beside the Kelvin, broadleaved trees manage to flourish, though no evergreen conifer could thrive. Tree planting is encouraged by the Glasgow Tree-Lovers Society, which has found that several kinds of flowering and fruiting trees are sufficiently resistant to the prevailing smoke. For example the Swedish whitebeam, *Sorbus scandica*, grows in George Square, at the very heart of the city.

Glasgow and the neighbouring industrial towns are the main consuming centres for timber in Scotland. Despite the ease with which wood can be imported to the Clyde from overseas, Scottish-grown material is winning a firm place. Much is converted from the log in local sawmills, particularly softwood for making packing cases for the export of machinery, or for engineering patterns. Much, too, is used in shipbuilding, and when those great liners, the *Queen Mary* and the *Queen Elizabeth*, were under construction at Clydebank, their hulls were supported on stout "shores" or poles of Scottish-grown larch. All the pit props and other timber used in the Scottish coalfields now come from Scottish forests, which thus contribute substantially to the prosperity of this closely industrialised region.

Renfrewshire

The small county of Renfrew has 7,000 acres under woodland, equivalent to 5 per cent of its surface. Nearly all these woods are privately owned, and most lie on the low ground or the foothills in the centre of the county, between Paisley, Johnstone, Kilmacolm, Port Glasgow, and Renfrew. The western moors towards the Hill of Stake are treeless. Around Langbank, where road and railway follow the broad course of the lower Clyde opposite Dumbarton, grow some fine policy woods of beech and sycamore, while a large plantation of Sitka spruce borders the railway between Bishopton and Paisley. Away to the west, beyond Cloch Point, there are tall woods of pine, larch, and Norway spruce near Inverkip, on braes that face west towards the open Firth of Clyde. In this district, too, the Forestry Commission is establishing its new Leapmoor Forest of 1,500 acres.

Dunbartonshire

The shire that takes its name from the town of Dumbarton is an odd assortment of lands—part Highland, part Lowland, that look as though they were left over from other counties, like awkward pieces of some giant jigsaw puzzle. Let us start in the west, at Kilcreggan on the Rosneath Peninsula, west of Helensburgh.

The Rosneath Peninsula consists of a long narrow ridge of hill pastures, but the broken slopes on either side hold a number of scattered woods, and several of these have been formed by the Forestry Commission into its Garelochhead Forest, which takes its name from the village at the northern neck of the peninsula. The total extent of this forest is 4,000 acres; much of the land carried rough oak and birch scrub when it was acquired, but the principal trees now being planted are Scots pine, Norway spruce, and Japanese larch.

From the anchorage north of Helensburgh, where great oil tankers discharge their cargoes into the long pipe-line that runs right across Scotland to the refineries at Grangemouth, we may follow road and railway up the steep shores of Loch Long. Right up to Arrochar there is a continuous fringe of oak and birch scrub, which in days gone by was coppiced to provide charcoal wood and tan bark; but scarcely any of these steep braes are now worked as productive forest.

Loch Lomondside—*Plates 12 to 16*

At Arrochar we turn east to cross the narrow isthmus of low ground that leads to Loch Lomond. It was over this gap that, in 1263 A.D., King Haakon's Norsemen dragged their galleys to ravage the settlements on the islands and shores of Loch Lomond, where the Scots had thought themselves secure. From Tarbet the narrow northern arm of the loch winds ever deeper into the Highlands, and again the road and the railway that cling to its steep shore are fringed with oak and birch, while alders clothe the banks of the burns and the shores of the loch itself. To the west, the peaks of Ben Vane and Ben Vorlich rise to heights around 3,000 feet, and between them lies Loch Sloy, now the storage reservoir for the huge hydro-electric power station that we pass on the loch side. At Ardlui the head of the loch is gained, and Dunbartonshire extends for only a mile or so beyond. But since we are following the waters rather than the county divisions we will go on, into Perthshire, to explore Glen Falloch.

Here we shall meet, for the first time, a substantial fragment of the old native Caledonian Forest of Scots pine, that once overspread the glens right through the Highlands. Only scattered survivors remain, usually on the less accessible crags, where their felling appeared hardly worth while. Sturdy red-barked giants topped by shaggy crowns of dark purplish-green foliage, they flourish here despite the high rainfall, exposure, and peaty soil that are often said to discourage the Scots pine in the west of the country. The broadleaved woodland that grows more plentifully around them is largely of the sessile oak, *Quercus petraea*, the species that is more at home on poor soils of the Highlands than is the pedunculate oak, *Quercus robur*, commonly planted in

PLATE 13
The westward view across Loch Lomond from Rowardennan showing the pleasure steamer and the wooded slopes of the Dunbartonshire shore.

the richer Lowlands to the east. There is much birch scrub also, with alder and willow on the wetter ground, making up this intriguing stretch of indigenous woodland that lies between Ardlui and Crianlarich. Native ancestry is also claimed for a few clumps of pines on the west shore of Loch Lomond, close to Tarbet.

From Tarbet, we can go south along the shore road that commands such glorious views of Ben Lomond, away across the water to the east. The estate of Luss, owned by the Colquhoun family, which lies around Luss village, is noted for its plantations of larch. The Forestry Commission also has a small property on this western shore. The islands that stud the lower and broader end of the loch are clothed for the most part with oakwoods that have been cut over for firewood,

charcoal wood, and tan bark in the past, and are now preserved mainly for their scenic value. But one of them, Inchture, is properly *Innis an t' Iubhar*, or the island of the yew trees, and yews are still plentiful on it, as they were when first it gained its Gaelic name.

The outflow from Loch Lomond is soon to be controlled by a barrage across the River Leven, at Balloch; this will enable large volumes of drinking water to be drawn from it, without affecting its surface level.

Dumbarton, Kirkintilloch, and Cumbernauld

The low south-eastern shore of the loch, between the River Endrick that flows into it near Balmaha, and the River Leven that flows out of it at Balloch to wind down to the Clyde, bears broadleaved trees—alder, oak,

27

PLATE 14
Loch Lomond at Rowardennan, Queen Elizabeth Forest Park. Natural woods of oak, birch and hazel reach far up the slopes of Ptarmigan (centre) an outlying peak of Ben Lomond (right).

beech, and sycamore, and Balloch Park, which is open to the public and overlooks a busy anchorage for pleasure boats of all kinds, holds fine avenues and policy plantings of broadleaved trees. At Ross Priory, near the Endrick, the Forestry Commission is engaged on experiments in the establishment of broadleaved trees suited to local conditions. Wych elm is a common tree in this region, and the probable derivation for the name of the River Leven is the Gaelic name for this tree, which is *leamhan*, pronounced "leven".

Dumbarton town, where the Leven winds below two breast-shaped hills to join the Clyde, was long well known as the birthplace of steel craft of moderate size, such as passenger boats that plied on the Clyde itself and also on short cross-channel trips to Ireland or the Continent. But its origins as a ship-building centre go right back to wooden craft, and in the National Maritime Museum at Greenwich there is a fine contemporary picture showing the construction of naval vessels here

about the year 1800. Much sound Scottish oak came down the Clyde and the Leven to form the great frameworks of ribs, crooks, and bends that went into the huge hulls assembled on these shores, just above the level of the tide.

The rest of the main portion of Dunbartonshire, between Dumbarton and Glasgow, holds remarkably little woodland. The Kilpatrick Hills still appear bleak and treeless, though Commission afforestation schemes are now under way there. Only a sprinkling of oak, ash, and beech grows along the Clyde shores near Bowling.

Away to the east, the detached portion of the county, beyond Kirkintilloch, holds a number of scattered woods. In particular, there is a long narrow glen holding a good deal of wych elm, ash, oak, and sycamore, for a mile or more along the main railway line, which provides a pleasant sylvan interlude for the traveller from Glasgow or Carlisle going towards Stirling and the north.

28

Cumbernauld was once the centre of a large forest, which was eventually enclosed by palings, in such a way that a herd of wild white cattle were confined therein; but this herd is now extinct. Cumbernauld today is the site of one of Scotland's "new towns", built to accommodate the surplus population moving out from Glasgow. On its outskirts, 1,600 acres of old woods and moorland have been taken over by the Commission to form a new Cumbernauld Forest, while nearer at hand the new town authority has planted scenic shelterbelts.

Queen Elizabeth Forest Park—*Plates 10, 12 to 20, and 36*

Much of the eastern shores of Loch Lomond, lofty Ben Lomond itself, and the rugged expanse of hills that stretches over to Loch Ard, Aberfoyle, romantic Ben Venue, and the Trossachs, were formed, in 1953, into a new Forest Park. For twenty years before that the foresters had been busy at the Loch Ard and Achray Forests, around Aberfoyle. The acquisition of the Rowardennan Forest on Loch Lomondside provided a unique opportunity to make one of the most popular portions of the Highlands into a region of recognised public access, and the new Park received its name to commemorate Her Majesty's Coronation. The combined extent of these three forests is 45,000 acres, or some seventy square miles; three-fifths of this, or some 26,500 acres, carries plantations, down in the glens. Many mountainsides are too high for afforestation, and there will thus remain around 18,500 acres of grand hill walking country, above the tree line, which is within easy reach of Glasgow and the neighbouring towns.

The western face of this great Forest Park can be reached in summer by taking the train to Balloch, and then the loch steamer to Balmaha or Rowardennan pier.

The road route from Glasgow runs through the village of Drymen, and then turns west past the extensive broadleaved woodlands and parks of the Buchanan Estate, which run down to the River Endrick. Here once stood the enormous Victorian mansion called Buchanan Castle, a seat of the Duke of Montrose, but now demolished.

North of Drymen, where the moors come down to the narrow strath, stands Garadhban Forest, a long narrow strip of plantations of spruces, pines, and larches, covering 3,500 acres. At Balmaha, where the bus route ceases, the road comes suddenly out on the shores of Loch Lomond, beside a little inlet where pleasure craft lie at anchor. Thence it winds over a hillock, through the little Pass of Balmaha, to give a glorious view of the ten tree-covered islets that stud the clear waters of the loch. To the north the great peaks stand in all their grandeur, and you can see right up the water and far over to the west into Argyll.

Rowardennan Forest

The road drops again to the loch shore, and a couple of miles farther on passes the public camping ground near the Cashel Burn. For eight miles on, the loch shores are fringed with oak coppices, which were worked until late in the last century for their valuable tan-bark. In 1841 the Duke of Montrose held 3,000 acres of these woods, and every year he cut 120 acres, working through them all every 25 years, by which time each plot had grown tall again. This brought him a steady income of nearly £1,000 a year—no mean sum when the labourers engaged earned only a shilling a day! The tree cutting was done by men, but their wives left their cottages, and the children deserted the little school at Balmaha, to strip the bark from the stems, for it would only come away freely for a month or two in late spring, when the sap was flowing fast. The bark was sent by water, down Loch Lomond, the River Leven, and the Clyde to tanneries in Glasgow, Ireland, or the West of England. Charcoal from peeled logs supported an active iron smelting industry.

Now there are so few people left on this shore that when tree planting began in 1952 the first essential step was to build new houses for the forest staff. Some of the oak is good enough to be left to stand as timber, but most will be gradually replaced with larches, spruces, and pines. Today there is no market in Scotland for oak bark—and only a small one for charcoal, but these slopes can produce very large volumes of softwood timber.

As you follow the road through the gnarled and twisted oaks you may chance to see the agile grey squirrel, an American alien who has made himself at home in a narrow belt across central Scotland. He is not loved by the forester, for although he may be forgiven for eating acorns, beech nuts, and pine seeds, his habit of stripping the bark from young sycamores, beeches, and ashes can cause the ruin of splendid trees.

The road ends at Rowardennan, where there is an inn, a youth hostel, and piers for the loch steamer. North of that point there is only a footpath along the steep shore, below the crags of Ptarmigan, to Inversnaid, six miles away. There another public road reaches the lochside, beside another inn.

Climbing Ben Lomond

Rowardennan is the starting point for the path that climbs steadily up Ben Lomond, 3,192 feet above sea level and 3½ miles distant, a long pull of three hours for an average walker. But at the summit you feel a true mountaineer, for you gaze ahead upon range after range of bens running far to north and west; nearly all of them are over three thousand feet, and the four-thousand foot Ben Nevis, highest in Scotland, can be descried away on the north-west horizon.

Only a few yards to the north, Ben Lomond breaks away below your feet in sheer crags and precipices.

To the south and east the outlook lies over the

PLATE 15
The snowbound summit of Ben Lomond, 3,192 feet and the highest point of the Queen Elizabeth Forest Park, showing the sheer crags of the north face.

homelier country of Strath Endrick, Stirlingshire, and the upper reaches of the Forth. For here, though only five miles, as the eagle flies, from the saltwater of Loch Long, you stand on a watershed parting Forth and Clyde. A sturdy rambler can descend eastwards to cross the miles of high, peaty moors to the vast plantations of Loch Ard and Achray Forests.

Aberfoyle, Loch Ard, The Trossachs—*Plates 17, 20 and 36*

These two forests, centred on Aberfoyle, draw their names from two lovely tree-fringed lochs. They extend north-west to Loch Chon, south beyond the old stone keep of Duchray Castle, and east to the Lake of Menteith. From Aberfoyle, you may take "The Duke's Road", built by a former Duke of Montrose, over to the Trossachs and Loch Katrine, surveying as you go

Loch Drunkie, Loch Venachar, and Loch Achray, and all the way you will have thriving young plantations for company. The David Marshall Lodge, set on a hillcrest above Aberfoyle, was gifted by the Carnegie Trustees to provide a fitting halting point, for rest, refreshment, and a magnificent outlook.

The birch and oak of the old native woods have been largely replaced by larch and spruce, but the native Scots pine still plays a part, and a pleasing feature is the arrangement of the new trees to suit the natural variation of the ground. Where bracken grew, the forester has planted Japanese larch, blue-green in summer but showing rust-red bare branches in winter; he has replaced the dusky-brown heather with slaty-blue pine, and the green of grass and rush with the deeper green of Norway spruce. A rich mosaic of colour

30

PLATE 16
Looking north from Ben Lomond in the Queen Elizabeth Forest Park, over the upper reaches of Loch Lomond towards Ben Laoigh, Ben Dubh-craig and Ben More (right).

remains, altered in detail but showing a fresh range of pastel shades to delight the traveller under the ever-changing play of sun and cloud over the lofty hills.

Yes, the scenery of this famous Trossachs country has gained from the advent of the conifers that look so thoroughly at home amid its crags and torrents. But though the forester is heedful of amenity, especially in a tourist centre such as this, he is naturally more concerned with the speed of growth and rate of timber output from his crops. Here the results are gratifying, for on all the better ground the faster conifers, including Japanese larch, Douglas fir, and Sitka spruce, start away so well that thinnings are needed after only fifteen years. Hence an increasing stream of timber for farms, mines and pulp mills flows out from the Loch Ard woods.

This has meant a radical change in local employment and population. When Sir Walter Scott came to Aberfoyle in 1790, to draw the inspiration that gave the world his poem the *Lady of the Lake*, and his romantic story of *Rob Roy*, the glens were peopled with sturdy crofters drawing a living from their cattle, their crops, and their oakwoods. Subsequently, a regime of sport and hill sheep was accompanied by emigration and a drastic decline of population; the tourists supported a handful of roadmen, drivers, and innkeepers, but nobody else. Forestry has brought constant employment for more than a hundred men which, after allowing for their families, means a community of over four hundred people. Two new housing estates, one at Kinlochard and another at Bravall, have been needed to house these new Highlanders, while elsewhere many steadings have been given a fresh lease of life.

31

PLATE 17
Loch Ard, west of Aberfoyle, on the Perthshire side of the Queen Elizabeth Forest Park, looking west towards the snowclad peak of Ben Lomond.

Aberfoyle and the Trossachs are, of course, readily reached by road from Glasgow or Stirling, and these approaches give to thousands of visitors their finest view of the new developments in Scottish forestry. Loch Katrine, just to the north west, provides Glasgow with its water, and on its shores there are old oakwoods and modern plantations of conifers established by the Glasgow Corporation, but now tended by the Forestry Commission.

Approaching Aberfoyle from Glasgow, Loch Ard Forest first comes into view as one tops the hill near the well-known cross-roads called Ballat Box; a rich, dappled mosaic of colour is seen clothing the high ridge of the Menteith Hills. Then the route descends to the strath of the infant River Forth. After a left turn, a mile short of Aberfoyle, you travel between larchwoods on the hillsides and old oakwoods preserved as part of the

modern forest, down on the low ground to reach Aberfoyle itself.

Aberfoyle to Stronachlachar and Inversnaid

A mile west of Aberfoyle village, and just to the left of the road, the Forth itself is born through the blending of the Duchray Water with the Water of Chon, for that great river has no named source of its own. Thence the road winds through the little Pass of Aberfoyle to gain the shores of Loch Ard, fringed with alders and spruces, and bearing a grim old keep, Duke Murdoch's Castle, on a rocky islet.

On through more oakwoods, past the new forestry houses at Kinlochard, to ascend through the spruce-woods around Loch Chon. Then the forest is left behind, and a bleak, barren, rainswept and windswept upland ensues. This inhospitable waste is the gathering ground for the Loch Katrine waters, and the loch itself comes into view near Stronachlachar, down on the left. Here was the MacGregor's stronghold, but one cannot imagine a rabbit, still less an outlaw, finding cover on its bare slopes today; the answer must be that three hundred years ago it carried a forest cover of oak, pine, and hazel, which has been bared since then by the busy teeth of the sheep, consuming every seedling.

After passing Loch Arklet, now a reservoir to augment Loch Katrine, the road falls steeply to Inversnaid on Loch Lomond, a few miles north of Rowardennan Forest. There it ends, for there is nowadays no regular ferry crossing.

If you start from Stirling there are two routes to the Forest Park, one past the Lake of Menteith to Aberfoyle, the other through Callander to the Trossachs and the lower end of Loch Katrine; the two are linked by the Duke's Road through Achray Forest. Some three miles out of Callander the broad expanse of Loch Venachar reveals the young forest rising high above its southern shore, and there are outlying woods on the northern side. A few miles farther on, just beyond the Brig o' Turk, the traveller sees before him the incomparable view of calm Loch Achray and rocky Ben Venue, which has been recorded by hundreds of artists and thousands of cameras. Here the pattern of the trees—birch, oak and alder beside the loch, spruce, pine and larch on the distant braes—combine with the wonderful interplay of sun and cloud, rain or snow, and mist over the peaks, to produce effects that are rarely the same for ten

PLATE 18
The David Marshall Lodge, a halting point above Aberfoyle, commands a wide view over Loch Ard Forest towards the Campsie Fells.

Climbing the Duke's Road out of Aberfoyle, on the way to the Trossachs.

minutes together. For this is the borderland between the rainy, windy west and the sunnier east of Scotland, where wind and cloud wage weird battles amid the hills, and every peak produces its own weather.

Though the whole countryside, which here forms the headwaters of the River Teith, is called The Trossachs, this name is more particularly applied to the rocky defile that leads from Loch Achray to Loch Katrine—a picturesque pass where a fragment of the old oak and birch woods, that once beautified far more of these glens, has survived to delight the modern traveller. The red deer are still here too, and the golden eagle, though you are unlikely to see either in summer when the tourists throng the roads. Ben Venue is still the home of a herd of wild goats.

Carron Valley and the Campsie Fells—*Plate 34*

The Campsie Fells form the broad bastion of central Scotland that rises in steep slopes from the lowlands between Glasgow, Aberfoyle, Stirling, and Falkirk. Road and rail alike wind round below them, and their heights, though often seen, are seldom visited. In their heart lies a broad basin, its floor 800 feet above the level of the sea, which has been dammed and flooded to form a great reservoir. This Carron Valley scheme supplies Falkirk and the neighbouring towns with their drinking water, which comes from tributaries of the little River Carron, which runs down to the Forth. Around the reservoir, the Carron Valley Forest hold 6,000 acres of sprucewoods, all planted since 1937. They go up to a height of 1,500 feet on the slopes of the Meikle Bin, 1,870 feet. Growth has been good, except for a strange setback that affected part of the forest in 1954, when a great plague of field voles sprang up. After eating down all the grass they began to bark the young trees, which perished over substantial areas. The plague was halted in a remarkable fashion for scores of short-eared owls flew in from surrounding parts, nested in their usual way, and fed hundreds of hungry nestlings on field voles.

Away to the south, six miles north west of Kirkintilloch, the small forest of Lennox has been planted on an outlier of the Campsies. It covers 800 acres, and afforestation with Sitka spruces began in 1929. Growth has been slow, partly because the soil is a heavy intractable clay, and partly because this region, on the fringe of the Clyde Valley's mines and industries, is subject to severe smoke pollution. Winds, too, blow keenly over this hillock, and many young trees have been lost through windblow; while 126 acres were burnt by German incendiary bombs during the war. Nearby are the woods of Lennox Castle, now a hospital, which extend to 400 acres and are largely of Sitka spruce.

Running west from Lennoxtown is the well wooded valley of Strathblane, which holds a succession of large private estates right down to Killearn. Here grows a wealth of broadleaved trees, particularly oak, ash, beech, and sycamore, with larch and pine on the braes.

North of the Campsies the vast peaty waste of Flanders Moss stretches along the winding River Forth, and in its heart the Forestry Commission is draining and planting substantial areas. Elsewhere the peat lies too thick, and holds too much water, to attract the reclaimers, whether they be seeking farmland, forest land, or peat for fuel.

The north-western foothills of the Campsies, from Kippen round to Stirling and Bannockburn, are closely tree-clad. Most of these woods are in private ownership, and the estate of Touch holds notable woods of oak, sycamore, ash, Douglas fir, and Norway spruce. Close

PLATE 20
Loch Katrine and Ben Venue in the Trossachs, with Ellen's Isle and natural woods of pine and birch.

by, the Commission is developing a new forest called Garshelloch, which covers 800 acres of the Gargunnock Hills.

The west of Stirlingshire, where it borders the open reaches of the Forth, is now much industrialised, and studded with coal mines. But several of the large estates have continued to maintain their woods; beside Falkirk, for example, the Callendar Estate carries thriving crops of Scots pine, Douglas fir, Sitka spruce and European larch. There is much beech and elm hereabouts also, and the rocky crag north of Stirling town, on which stands the Wallace Monument, is clothed with oak, ash, and wych elm.

PLATE 21
The winding course of the tidal River Tay, looking east from Kinnoull Hill in Kinfauns Forest, high above Perth.

4. Perthshire

Map: page 48

The vast Highland county of Perthshire, embracing the basin of the great River Tay, is often regarded as the cradle of forestry in Scotland. It was on its great estates, and particularly those of the Dukes of Atholl, that the big planting schemes of the eighteenth and nineteenth centuries were developed. Every aspect of forest management has received attention here; big nurseries for raising planting stock have been established; policy woods and specimen trees have been tended with particular care; plans for management and schemes of natural regeneration have long been worked out; saw-mills and timber utilisation are well developed; outdoor educational centres have been established; and the woods have been visited by generations of university forestry students and members of forestry societies.

Since 1919 the Forestry Commission has taken an increasing share in afforestation in Perthshire, mainly on lands where private proprietors were unable to extend their work. A fascinating account of the private estate woods and policies eighty-five years ago is to be found in the book: *Woods, Forests, and Estates of Perthshire*, written by Thomas Hunter, editor of the *Perthshire Constitutional*, in 1883.

Most of the county's woods are described in this chapter, but those in the south-west, near Glen Falloch and the Trossachs, were reviewed in the previous one.

Perth and the Lower Tay—*Plate 21*

The old city of Perth, rich in history, has a romantic situation in a gap which the broad River Tay has cut through a long ridge of basalt hills. Through this gap the river breaks out from its broad and fertile lower strath to gain its long tidal firth. On these hills, overlooking the city, stands the young Kinfauns Forest, which draws its name from the castle and village of Kinfauns. Its planting was begun in 1933, and it now comprises 1,100 acres in four blocks.

The most prominent woods stand on Kinnoull Hill, 729 feet, just east of Perth; a public path winds up through the larchwoods to its summit, where there is a direction indicator serving as a guide to one of the finest landscapes in all broad Scotland. The whole south-western face of the Grampians is in view to the north and west, while the scene extends over Strathmore, the Sidlaws, the Firth of Tay, Fife with its Lomond Hills, the Ochils, and Strath Earn. Below your feet the basalt cliffs fall in sheer precipices to the banks of the Tay, where road and railway wind through a narrow gap to gain the fertile Carse of Gowrie; you may look down on trains, cars, and coasting steamers dwarfed by the dizzy height. Kinnoull Hill and the neighbouring Binn Hill are each crowned with a false ruin or "folly", built by a former landowner, one of the Earls of Moray, on the model of the castles of the Rhine. The deception created by these mock watch towers is complete; you are momentarily transported to the great German river and the scene becomes oddly alien.

A second portion of Kinfauns Forest lies on hills farther east, north of Glencarse village; there is a third portion called Paddockmuir Wood, right on the banks of the Tay, south-east of Glencarse. The fourth block stands on the farther side of the Tay, on Moncreiffe Hill, close to the road that runs from Perth to Bridge of Earn and Edinburgh, through the well-wooded Pass of Glencarse. The main trees grown at Kinfauns are Scots pine, European larch, and Sitka spruce. There are also hardwood plantings, mainly of oak and beech, and the older plantations have reached the thinning stage. An arboretum on Kinnoull Hill, planted in 1924, includes fifty-nine different kinds of trees. Kinnoull Hill is also the site of a Roman or Pictish camp, while Moncreiffe Hill is topped by a Pictish fort.

The triangle of land between Perth, Dunkeld, and Blairgowrie is remarkably well wooded. It has a bed-rock of Old Red Sandstone which in places gives a highly fertile soil devoted to the raising of raspberries, seed potatoes, barley, and other demanding crops, or to the fattening of beef cattle. But where the bedrock nears the surface the thin soil has been found fit only for forest trees. Little natural woodland remains, but the planting lairds had clothed with prosperous conifer plantations the poor moorland that was left, after grazing and burning had disrupted the primeval forest. Large acreages were cleared in the two world wars, but replanting by private owners and the Commission has been on an equally generous scale. Today the wide sweep of the Tay round by Meikleour and Murthly is bordered by a series of plantations, on one bank or the other, for twenty miles. The climate of these southward-facing slopes is warm and genial, the soils are reasonably good by forestry standards, and satisfactory growth is secured.

Monks Planted Forests—500 Years Ago

During the Middle Ages much of this region was known as the Forest of Campsie. In 1171 the Scottish King William the Lion gave the monks of Coupar Abbey, at Coupar Angus, timber for their buildings. There are clauses in later medieval leases of this wood insisting on the planting of trees and protection against stock. The gardeners at the Abbey were bound to keep eleven beds of young trees, each 24 feet long, and to weed and manure them until they were four years old and ready to be set out in plantations. About the year 1470 the forests owned by Coupar Abbey included woods in Strathardle, the Forest of Forter in Glenisla, and the woods of Murthly and Inverack. Little is known of the composition of these woods, but it appears likely that broadleaved trees—oak, wych elm, ash and birch, had a leading share in the straths, with pine and birch higher up. The Forest Keepers were expressly permitted to depasture cattle in the woods; so by inference we can say that crofters' cattle were supposed to be kept out. The later decline of these forests was doubtless due to the introduction of sheep, and to the breakdown of monastic control after the Reformation.

Perth was for many years the centre of a large nursery trade, which supplied the neighbouring estates with the thousands of young trees required for their planting schemes. Many rare and curious kinds were imported, usually as seed, during the nineteenth century, from all

PLATE 22
The shapely bridge that carries the Perth–Inverness road, A.9 over the Tay at Dunkeld, with Craigvinean Forest and the Atholl Estate woodlands beyond.

The view south over Dunkeld and the River Tay, from the Hermitage towards Birnam, showing part of Craigvinean Forest and woodlands on the Atholl Estate.

the temperate regions of the world. As early as 1880, the nurserymen had discovered that larch and pine from Scottish-grown seed gave better results than many imported strains; recent tests have amply confirmed this view.

Just to the north of Perth, on the east bank of the Tay, stands Scone Palace, famous as the ancient resting place of the Stone of Destiny on which all the Scottish kings were crowned until the invasion of Edward I in 1296; this stone now rests below the Coronation Chair in Westminster Abbey. Scone is now the seat of the Earl of Mansfield, whose estate includes extensive woodlands fine policy grounds, and an arboretum.

Notable trees include a sycamore, reputedly planted by Mary Queen of Scots, which achieved a girth of 13 feet and a height of 63 feet in 300 years growth.

Ledmore Nursery—*Plates 24 and 46*

Strathord Forest consists of several blocks of woodland around the little town of Bankfoot, midway between Perth and Dunkeld. Most of the ground is former woodland that was cleared of tree crops in the 1939–45 war, but some poor hill land has also been afforested. Since 1945, replanting with Scots pine, spruces, Douglas fir and larches has made steady progress, and plantations now cover 1,600 acres. These wooded sandstone hills, which rise to 400 feet above sea level, command fine views of the Sidlaw, Ochil, and Grampian ranges, and the fertile straths closer at hand.

Within Strathord Forest is the big Ledmore Nursery, which lies along a by-road, three miles south of Bankfoot, and extends to 117 acres. It was established in 1946 for the raising of the millions of young trees needed every year for forest planting in Central Scotland; this spot was selected because of its fertile sandy soil and congenial climate, with skilled labour near at hand. A feature of subsequent developments has been the mechanisation of most of the heavier work by devices thought out and perfected by Mr. A. Rose, the forester in charge. The whole nursery has been planned to make easy the driving of tractors and power tools; roads have been carefully spaced, working sections made as long as possible to save turning, and beds laid out at widths to suit tractors. The number of people employed varies from twenty to thirty.

If we follow the course of a young tree through Ledmore Nursery, we find that it starts as a seed sown by an automatic power drill, and is promptly covered by grit from an automatic distributor. After it has grown for a year or two to the "seedling" stage, its roots may be under-cut by another machine, or else loosened mechanically for ease of lifting. Transplanting to another bed will be done with the aid of the Ledmore lining-out plough, described below; after a further year or two of growth to the "transplant" stage, the little tree will again be prepared for removal by a mechanical plant lifter. Throughout its life in the nursery, it will be protected by selective chemical weedkillers; power-driven hoes will be used to eradicate the few weeds that spring up around it, while the ground in which it grows will have been prepared with the aid of tractor-drawn ploughs.

PLATE 24

Transplanting thousands of young spruce trees in Ledmore Nursery, Strathord Forest, close to Bankfoot in Perthshire. The tractor draws the ingenious lining-out machine invented by Head Forester Rose, which firms up earth against the roots of trees held in boards.

The transplanting or "lining-out" of young trees, even when done with the aid of transplanting boards, involves a series of steps which are normally done with hand tools by a skilled gang. But the Ledmore Lining-out Plough reduces them to one simple passage of a tractor and its implements over the bed. A set of lining-out boards, full of young trees, is placed along the edge of a trench; then the plough throws up earth against their roots, firms it up, and immediately excavates another trench, set a few inches away, for the next row. The boards are then removed, leaving a line of trees standing neatly in position, and are re-filled for the following row. The actual filling of the boards is done by nimble-fingered lads and girls, so that the human touch is not entirely lacking, even though the work proceeds with surprising speed. One plough can deal with 125,000 young trees in a day, and the cost of transplanting is only a few shillings a thousand.

Murthly and Birnam Wood

Just to the north of Bankfoot lie the extensive woodlands of the Murthly estate, owned by the Steuart-Fothringham family, and covering 3,800 acres; they rise from the banks of the Tay to a height of 1,300 acres on Birnam Hill near Dunkeld. This Birnam Hill, which still bears woods of oak and birch, is the same as that featured by Shakespeare in those immortal lines of *Macbeth*, when the witches assure the hero that:

"Macbeth shall never vanquish'd be until
 Great Birnam Wood to high Dunsinane Hill
 Shall come against him . . . "

Everyone knows how, in the last act, the soldiers of Macbeth's enemy Malcolm are ordered to hew down boughs from Birnam wood to conceal their actual numbers as they march forward to capture Dunsinane castle and slay Macbeth. Although in the play Dunsinane Hill is supposed to be within sight of Birnam Wood, the hill actually stands in the Sidlaws above Kinrossie, some ten miles away and not in direct view. Birnam estate has the stoutest oak recorded in Scotland, 21 feet 7 inches round though only 65 feet tall, and also Britain's stoutest sycamore, 22 feet 3 inches round and 85 feet tall.

In the first half of the nineteenth century Sir John Drummond Steuart, then Laird of Murthly, began the vigorous policy of tree planting that his successors have continued. There are now about 400 acres of broad-leaved trees, and some 3,400 of conifers. The estate has its own forest nursery and also a museum where specimens of timbers, cones, and seeds are preserved. It has pioneered the planting of new trees and provided most useful information for the Forestry Commission's records. One notable stand of the western hemlock, *Tsuga heterophylla*, had produced 10,200 hoppus feet of timber per acre when only 47 years old; it is still increasing in volume at the rate of 280 hoppus feet per acre, per year,

which is one of the highest rates known in the country for any kind of tree. There are also fine stands of hybrid larch and of western red cedar, *Thuja plicata*, from British Columbia.

The many fine specimen and avenue trees in the Murthly policies include a Sitka spruce 90 years old, which is 160 feet high and 15 feet 2 inches in girth at breast height, with a volume of 950 hoppus feet; it is reputed to be the biggest in Britain. Murthly also holds our tallest Serbian spruce, *Picea omorika*, 80 feet high, and our tallest American Mountain hemlock, *Tsuga mertensiana*, 88 feet. The biggest Douglas fir is 160 feet tall, 10 feet in girth, and 336 hoppus feet in volume. When a thinning was made in 90-year-old Douglas firs during the 1939–45 war, the average volume of each tree cut was 270 hoppus feet; their timber was all sound and of excellent quality. An avenue of yew trees along the Dead Man's Walk is 500 years old.

Blairgowrie, Stormont and Strathardle

Between Dunkeld and Blairgowrie lies one of the most beautiful wooded regions of the country. Set betwixt the winding Tay and the Grampians, it holds a chain of lovely lochs, and picturesque foothills clothed in woods of birch and pine.

Several fair-sized estates include expanses of woodland in this delectable region. The largest wooded stretch, which includes much oak, stands on Newtyle Hill, which rises to 1,041 feet above Birnam. There are other fine woods on the Glendelvine estate around the neat little village of Caputh and the lochside hamlet of Clunie.

The most remarkable example of tree growth hereabouts is the great beech hedge at Meikleour, reputed the finest hedge in the world. It is situated beside the main road from Perth to Blairgowrie, close to the point where it crosses the road from Dunkeld to Coupar Angus, and hence is easily found. Six hundred yards long, this hedge is over ninety feet high and some 220 years old, having been planted about 1746. It was regularly trimmed as an ordinary hedge for fifty years or so, then allowed to grow as it chose; being set close together on the edge of a wood, the trees drew one another up. Eventually it was trimmed back, and it is still clipped about once in every five years, with the aid of an extending tower ladder. It presents a splendid wall of living green foliage, and illustrates how the forester can shape the growth of trees to meet his ends.

The small town of Blairgowrie, and its sister village of Rattray on the eastern side of the River Ericht, is well known for its great raspberry raising industry; each summer when the crimson fruit ripens on the long rows of canes, a crowd of casual workers, including tinkers and students, arrive to gather in the luscious and juicy harvest. But the rich fertile, sandstone soils, facing south to the sun, lie only on one side of Blairgowrie.

41

Go a mile or so north or west and you cross the Highland Line into a hilly region of hard rock, poor soil, and moorland vegetation.

The braes to the west of Blairgowrie are known as Stormont, while the valley of the Ericht and the Ardle rivers on the north are called Strathardle. Anciently there was much more woodland hereabouts than is found today. In Stormont lay the Forest of Clunie, while to the east of Strathardle was the Forest of Alyth, with the Forest of Forter yet further east in Glen Isla. These are now little more than deer forests, diversified with occasional patches of oak, birch, and hazel scrub, or recently planted shelter blocks and belts of conifers. The famous road over to Deeside by the high pass of the Devil's Elbow, 2,000 feet up, runs from the Bridge of Cally in Strathardle up Glen Shee. As far as the Spittal of Glenshee it is bordered by trees and small woods, but thereafter it takes to the open moors. Until ski-ing became popular at Glenshee, this road was often snow-bound in winter, but now it is always kept open, to give access to one of Scotland's finest and most dependable snow slopes.

Around Bridge of Cally the young Blackcraig Forest extends up Strathardle and over Blackcraig Hill, 1,573 feet. Afforestation began here in 1930, and now embraces 3,300 acres of the braes, with spruces, larches, and pines as the principal trees. The older plantations are being thinned out; a system of forest roads has been built, and houses with smallholdings have been provided for the forest workers. Beyond the Blackcraig plantations, the road winds up through Kirkmichael village, and past the young Kindrogan Forest of 2,800 acres, towards Pitlochry, passing numerous shelterbelts planted where the high pastures neighbour the open moors. Kindrogan House is now the Scottish Field Study Centre, visited yearly by scores of biology students keen to see wild life in the woods and on the moors.

Atholl Estates: Dunkeld to Blair Atholl—*Plates 22 and 23*

The estates of the Dukes of Atholl, along the Tay valley from Dunkeld to Blair Atholl, hold a special place in the history of Scottish forestry. It was here that the great Planting Dukes clothed the hillsides with millions of larches, and here too that the vigorous and valuable Hybrid larch was first bred. The policy woods at Dunkeld House and Blair Castle hold magnificent specimen trees, and the estates have long maintained their own tree nurseries, sawmills, and wood preservation plants. The estates comprise 140,000 acres of land, but most of this is mountain and moor, and the woodland area is 7,500 acres, or roughly twelve square miles. This includes some 500 acres of broadleaved trees, mainly oak and birch, and 7,000 acres of conifer plantations, largely of larch and pine. The woods are spread over twenty miles of the Tay, Tummel, and Garry valleys, being

interspersed with national forests and woods on other estates; the whole forms one of the grandest stretches of wooded highland country in Britain.

Though conifers prevail today, there was a period in the past when oak coppices provided much of the estates' woodland income. Around the year 1798 the Duke of Atholl was cutting his coppices on a 25-year rotation; he received £40 to £54 an acre (probably the old Scots acre or 1.2 statute acres) at each cutting, equivalent to a rent of £2 10s. per acre a year. The men who felled the poles were paid one shilling a day, while the women who stripped off the bark got only seven-pence! The bark was sold to Perth tanneries for about one penny a pound, while the merchant recovered his expenses by selling the stripped poles as firewood or fence stakes. Such were the simple economics whereby the lairds grew rich, but this trade declined at the close of the nineteenth century, owing to the competition of imported tanning-bark extracts, and most oak coppices have now been converted to conifer plantations.

Few traces now survive of the conifer crops planted in the first era of expansion from 1738 to 1830, for most of that timber matured and was harvested during the two world wars of this century. The story began when a certain Colonel Menzies, of Meggernie in Glenlyon, presented sixteen of the then rare foreign larches to James, second Duke of Atholl. The tale goes that the gardeners first grew them in a greenhouse, but finding that they lost their leaves in winter, threw them out for dead. The hardy trees sprouted again next spring, and grew vigorously for over a century! Only one of the original trees, now a veteran of some 230 summers, survives, standing in the policies close to old Dunkeld Cathedral; it is 95 feet high and 16 feet round and still thrives. For many years larches remained scarce trees, and between 1740 and 1774 James, the Second Duke, and John, the Third Duke, were able to plant only about 1,000 acres.

After the Fourth Duke, known as "Planter John", succeeded in 1774, larch seed became more plentiful; apparently much was gathered by nurserymen from Scottish plantations, and the resulting crops showed great vigour and hardihood. Between 1774 and 1830, Planter John put 10,000 acres of land under larch, and brought the total of woodland on his estates, including oak, birch, and pine, to 15,500 acres, or roughly twice what it is today; it has been estimated that he used 15 million young larch trees. He also pioneered the use of larch timber in shipbuilding, and maintained that larch was an improver of hill pastures, permitting sweet grasses to flourish beneath its light shade. Much of his planting was done above the 700-feet contour. On the flanks of Creag nam Miall, 1,842 feet high, you may still find windswept clumps of small but aged larches, relics of his great schemes, which now afford nothing more than pasturage and shelter to wandering deer and blackfaced sheep. Dunkeld estate has the tallest European larch in Scotland, a tree 143 feet high and 7½ feet in girth.

In 1884 the Seventh Duke of Atholl brought home from Japan the seed of the Japanese larch, *Larix kaempferi*, then new to cultivation in Scotland. From this seed, eleven sturdy young trees were raised in the estate nurseries and planted along the road called The Avenue, running from Dunkeld town to Dunkeld House, below the Kennel Bank. There they still stand, being now eight-two years old (from seed); the largest specimen is 91 feet tall and 8 feet round.

As early as 1896, when these trees were only eleven years old, a Dunkeld forester named Brown gathered their seed, and sowed it next year in his Ladywell Nursery nearby. These seedlings grew with remarkable speed, but looked somehow different to their parents. Mr. H. J. Elwes, then the leading authority on forest trees, was called in to examine them, and at once suspected that they were hybrids; subsequently his collaborator Professor Augustine Henry of Dublin gave them the scientific name of *Larix eurolepis*. What had happened was that the female Japanese larch trees had been pollinated by some sturdy European larches growing nearby. A new race of trees, called the Dunkeld Hybrid larch, had been born.

The Atholl estate foresters hastened to make use of this new find, which grows strongly in plantations, and tolerates poorer soils than do the other larches. Considerable acreages are grown on these estates, as the hybrid vigour is maintained in large degree to the second generation—readily obtained from seed ripened by first generation trees. Other estates have taken up this tree with enthusiasm, and the Forestry Commission is now raising supplies of first generation seed in special orchards. One of the oldest plantations on the Atholl estates, when 48 years of age, was 86 feet high, had a standing volume of 3,000 (hoppus) cubic feet to the acre, and had produced altogether some 7,400 cubic feet, at the exceptionally high rate (for any larch) of 154 cubic feet per acre per year.

The Blair Castle portion of the Atholl estates consists mainly of a great block of plantations, largely of larches, between Glen Tilt and Glen Bruar, close to Struan. The policy grounds adjoining the grand old castle, built in the Scots baronial style, include a number of specimen trees reputed the tallest in the country. These include:

Japanese Larch, *Larix leptolepis*	105	feet
Hybrid Larch, *Larix eurolepis*	97	,,
Californian Red Fir, *Abies magnifica*	116	,,
Low's Silver Fir, *Abies lowiana*	134	,,
Colorado White Fir, *Abies concolor*	127	,,
Grand Silver Fir, *Abies grandis*	138	,,
Birch, *Betula pendula*	94	,,

All the firs come from the western regions of North America. An estimate of the volume of timber standing in that part of the policies known as Diana's Grove gave the amazing figure of 12,000 hoppus feet to the acre, all of which had been produced in the eighty years since the trees were planted in 1880.

The Bruar Water, which lies towards the western end of the Blair Atholl woods, has the distinction of being the subject of a poem by Burns, entitled: *The Humble Petition of Bruar Water to His Grace the Duke of Atholl*, in which the stream pleads for tree cover—a wish since granted:

"Would then my noble master please
    To grant my highest wishes,
He'll shade my banks wi' tow'ring trees
    And bonny spreading bushes."

New Forests in Atholl

The Forestry Commission has long been active in the valleys of the Tay, the Tummel and the Garry. In 1937, cleared woodland on the Atholl estates was acquired for re-planting, as Craigvinean Forest, which now covers 4,100 acres. All this forest lies on the west side of the Tay between Dunkeld and Logierait, running up the braes to Creag am Uamhaid, 1,623 feet; it is plainly in view from the railway and the two main roads up the strath, and the passer-by will also note the neat group of forest workers houses at Dalguise. The plantations, which are largely of larches, spruces, and Scots pine, have made good progress, and the older ones are already being thinned out. A network of roads to aid access and extraction of logs has been laid out on these steep hillsides, which include the crags of Craig Vinean itself.

Above Ballinluig, where Tay and Tummel meet, lies a triangle of high ground carrying some good plantations but also much birch scrub and heather moor. Here, between Pitlochry and Grandtully, the Commission began, in 1953, the formation of the Fonab section of Faskally Forest. This now covers 2,200 acres, including 500 acres of unplantable high moorland. Sitka spruce and lodgepole pine are the main trees grown.

Pitlochry, Faskally, Killiecrankie—*Cover picture*

The charming inland resort of Pitlochry was enriched, in 1953, by the creation of a great reservoir, called Loch Faskally, on its doorstep. This was the work of the North of Scotland Hydro-Electric Power Board, which built a great dam to hold back the waters of the Tummel, with a power-house below it. A second powerhouse at Cluny farther up the loch derives power from the water that once coursed over the Falls of Tummel nearby. When the Faskally Glen was drowned, much thought was taken to preserve amenities. The banks around the dam were landscaped, footbridges were built, provision was made for boating and fishing, and a salmon ladder was built to enable the fish to get upstream to their spawning grounds; the great fish can, in fact, be watched from an observation room. After the work of construction was over, the woodlands of the old Faskally Estate, formerly owned by the Butter family, were transferred to the Forestry Commission, together with Faskally House.

Faskally House has been transformed into a forestry educational centre, where trainees and supervisors receive both practical and classroom instruction for work in the Commission's forests or on private estates. (See cover picture.) Around it lie 186 acres of woodland which, when acquired, presented a varied pattern of fine old mixed policy timber, old oak, and young conifer. Since Faskally is so much in the public eye, this woodland is now managed under a selection system, whereby trees of varied ages, sizes, and species grow intermingled; the older individuals are felled as they mature, and a proportion of younger ones are likewise removed from time to time. Clear fellings are avoided, and re-planting is done in small areas at one time, mainly where insufficient seedlings fail to spring up naturally. Such methods of management can lead to high overall timber yields, but they call for much skill on the part of the forester in charge. The remainder of Faskally Forest, which extends in all to over 1,000 acres, consists of foothill slopes on Ben Vrackie, acquired for planting in 1955.

Just to the north of Faskally lies the famous Pass of Killiecrankie, a narrow defile leading into the higher reaches of the River Garry. Here road and railway wind through a narrow rocky gorge, now fringed with birch trees, although the pass draws its name from the Gaelic *coille criathannach*, meaning "the wood of the trembling trees", or aspens. The Pass, which was the scene of the famous battle in 1696, when "Bonnie Dundee" was killed in the moment of victory, is said to lie at the very heart of Scotland. It is now the property of the Scottish National Trust, which maintains paths and a parking ground to aid access by visitors.

Above Struan there are only one or two small plantations in the Commission's care, the highest being near Dalnacardoch Lodge. Both road and rail take to the open moors as they climb steadily up the Pass of Drumochter, leading over into the Spey valley and Badenoch. At 1,500 feet this pass carries the highest railway in Britain; though it is protected from the winter blizzards by snow fences, it often calls for snowploughs. The treeless state of the hills around—including the famous Sow of Athol and Boar of Badenoch that mark the boundary between the counties of Perth and Inverness—is not solely due to height and exposure. Grazing by sheep and deer are supplemented by the burning of the heather to improve its value as food for red grouse, a custom that leaves an artificial patchwork of grey and brown over the moors. Odd shelterbelts of Scots pine struggle to grow beside steadings, and much of the land could carry trees, though seldom as economic timber. The whole region is known as the Forest of Atholl, while a number of minor forests or stalker's beats carry local names.

At Struan, a side glen called Glen Errochty strikes off to the west, and in and around this glen the Commission has, since 1951, built up its vast Glenerrochty Forest, covering 12,000 acres. This runs up to heights around 1,600 feet, but no less than 6,000 acres are accounted unplantable; the remaining 6,000 acres are being afforested, largely with pines and spruces. A big dam traps the waters at the head of the glen, to divert them through a tunnel under the hills to a power station on the Tummel.

Strath Tummel and Queen's View—*Plates 25, 26 and p. iv*

Just below Killiecrankie a by-road strikes off west, crosses the Garry by a Bailey Bridge, and winds up past Bonskeid House to the famous Queen's View, so called because it once attracted the admiring gaze of Queen Victoria. This viewpoint, which now has a car park and a shelter pavilion built of Scots pine logs, is situated beside the road and looks westward up Loch Tummel, embowered in woods of birch and pine. The peaks of Beinn a' Chuallaich, 2,925 feet, on the north, and Schichallion, 3,547 feet, on the south, form a fitting frame. From this spot the road runs west for twenty-five miles up the elevated strath, all of it 600 feet or more above sea level, passing in turn Loch Tummel, the Dunalastair reservoir, and Loch Rannoch, to end at the lonely station of Rannoch, on the Highland Line from Glasgow to Fort William. There are trees the whole way —sometimes a mere fringe of birch, sometimes relics of old Caledonian pinewoods, and sometimes modern plantations. There are also huge hydro-electric works— dams, power stations, leats, and hidden tunnels, with a forest of tall pylons and overhead cables, which all form part of the great Tummel-Garry scheme of the North of Scotland Hydro-Electric Board. Sailing on Loch Tummel is a recent recreational development in a region that is becoming ever more popular for tourists.

Beyond the Queen's View, the road runs through the vast new forest called Allean, which was commenced in 1945; it covers 5,100 acres, including 1,000 of hill grazings, and the main trees planted are spruces, larches, pines and Douglas fir; it extends far up the braes around Tummel Bridge. The Falls of Tummel, owned by the National Trust for Scotland, lie lower down the river towards Faskally; they are surrounded by birchwoods, but much of their effect is lost, now that so much water is diverted through tunnels to yield power. The best approach to them is by the road on the south bank; there is also a path from Killiecrankie on their northern side.

NORTH

Glen Garry
South Laggan
Drumgask
Inshriach
Clunes
Strath Mashie
Glenfinnan
Leanachan
Corrour
Glen Loy
Glen Hurich
Fort William
Nevis
Glenerrochty
Glen Righ
Allean
Strontian
Rannoch
Glencoe
Black Corries
Kinloch Rannoch
Tummel Br.
Sunart
Glenduror
Faskally
Glencoe
Creran
Drummond Hill
Keltneyburn
Aberfeldy
Gualachulain
Loch Etive
Kenmore
Barcaldine
Loch Tay
Connel Ferry
Fearnoch
Dalmally
Keillour
Glenorchy
Balquhidder
Gilmert
Crianlarich
Lochearnhead
Crieff
Inverinan
Glendochart
St. Fillans
Dalmally
WEST
Strathyre
Raera
Loch Ard
Inverliever
Loch Awe
Torrie
Inveraray
Ardgartan
Callander
Greenloaning
Eredine
Achray
Kilmartin
Ford
Arrochar
Dunblane
Loch Goil
Strachlan
Strachur
Rowardennan
Aberfoyle
Thornhill
Kilmichael
Newton
Glenbranter
Minard
Kippen
Alloa
Garadhban
Garshelloch
STIRLING
Devilla
Knapdale
Loch Eck
Lochgilphead
Asknish
Benmore
Garelochhead
Loch Lomond
Dunipace
Kilmory
Glendaruel
Glenfinart
Carron Valley
Auchenbreck
Jamestown
Cumbernauld
FALK
Tighnabruaich
Dunoon
Port Glasgow
Lennox
Cumbernauld
GREENOCK
Dumbarton
Corlarach
CLYDE
CLYDEBANK
Achaglachgach
Leapmoor
PAISLEY
GLASGOW
AIRDRIE
Rothesay
COATBRIDGE
MOTHERWELL
WISHAW
HAMILTON

MAP I FORESTS OF CENTRAL SCOTLAND: WESTERN

Most of the Forests shown lie in the West Conservancy (Headquarters, Glasgow). Those at the top right are Perthshire Forests in the East Conservancy (Headquarters, Aberdeen). Forests at top left are in the North Conservancy (Headquarters, Inverness) and will be described in a separate guide book (in preparation). (Scale 10 miles to 1 inch.)

45

MAP 2   FORESTS OF SOUTHERN SCOTLAND

Most of the Forests shown lie in the South Conservancy (Headquarters, Dumfries). Those north of the upper diagonal line are in the West Conservancy (Headquarters, Glasgow); the eastern ones are described herein;

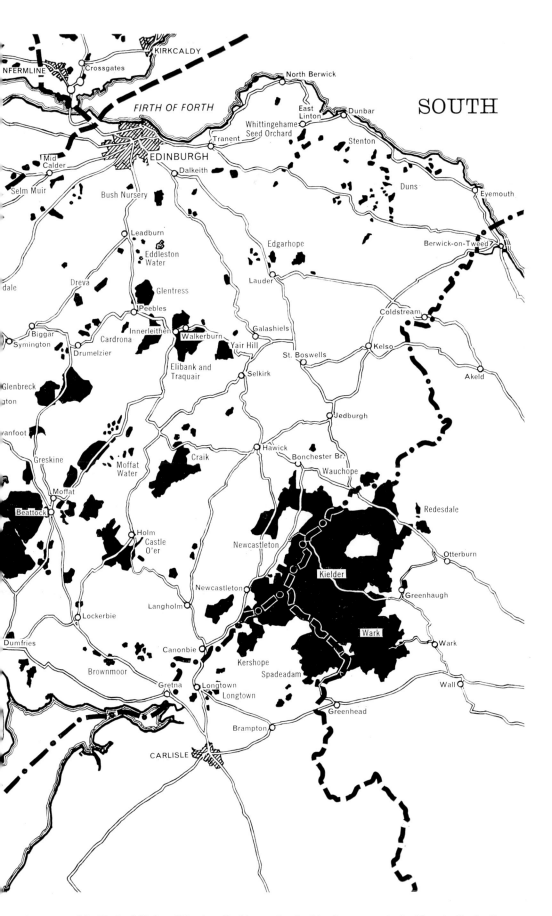

SOUTH

those west of the Firth of Clyde will be described in another booklet (in preparation). Note the Border Forest Park around Kielder on the English Border. (Scale: 10 miles to 1 inch.)

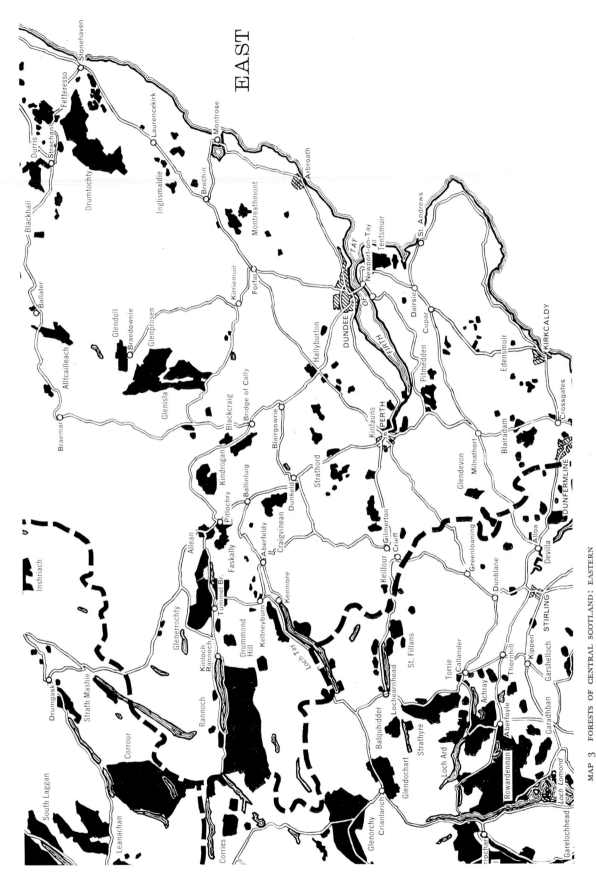

MAP 3 FORESTS OF CENTRAL SCOTLAND: EASTERN

Most of the Forests shown lie in the East Conservancy (Headquarters, Aberdeen); those west of the Dundee–Pitlochry road are described in the present booklet while the others appear in the *Guide to the Forests of North East Scotland* (HMSO 5s. od.). (Scale: 10 miles to 1 inch).

48

PLATE 25
Looking north across Loch Tummel towards Allean Forest, north of Pitlochry.

Loch Rannoch—*Pages ii and vi*

Loch Rannoch, now controlled as a reservoir, is a grand upland sheet of water, ten miles long by one mile wide. The main road along its northern shore passes small woods of birch and pine, while the by-road that follows its south bank goes through one of the most famous survivals of the Caledonian pinewoods—the Black Wood of Rannoch. This is now included within the Commission's immense Rannoch Forest, which has a total area of 47,500 acres, though only 13,500 acres rank as tree-growing land. The northern section of this Forest consists of some 600 acres on the north shore of Loch Rannoch, close to Craiganour Lodge; the remainder stretches far to the west, and also along the southern shore around Dall and Camghouran, reaching far up

the north face of Ben Lawers. Afforestation began in 1947 and the main trees planted are Scots and lodgepole pines, spruces and larches; to house the forest workers, a group of thirteen houses has been built at Kinloch Rannoch. The Black Wood, which now covers 670 acres, or just over one square mile, half way along the southern shore, receives the exceptional care that its long history merits. Loch Rannoch is 675 feet above the sea, and the pinewoods run up to 1,200 feet elevation.

In the days of Robert the Bruce, one of the King's henchmen, a chieftain of the Robertson clan, nick-named Duncan the Fat, married a daughter of the Earl of Lennox and so acquired the lands of Rannoch. From the fourteenth century down to 1857, these lands were held by the Robertsons, but following Prince Charles'

49

rebellion of 1745, they were administered from 1749 to 1784 by "The Commissioners of Forfeited Estates and Barons of the Exchequer". Records kept by that body shed considerable light on the history of this and other native pinewoods.

Although the wood itself was then uninhabited, at least by respectable members of the community, it had a tradition of harbouring outlaws and freebooters, and the operators of illicit whisky stills. There were crofting communities at Camghouran on the west and Carie on the east, who regularly pastured their flocks and herds in the Wood. Muirburn, or the burning-off of rough grass and heather in spring to encourage an early "bite" of fresh green grass, was a common event. Both practices made great inroads into the young regrowth of pine and birch trees, and in addition browsing by deer checked the seedlings. A custom prevailed of proprietors farming out such woods to "tacksmen", on payment of a yearly rental; in addition to the grazing, the tacksman was allowed to fell a stated number of trees. This number was supposed to be within the capacity of the wood to make good through natural regrowth, but in the absence of satisfactory records of growth, there was an obvious danger of overcutting. By risking overcutting, the proprietor could demand a higher rent, while the tacksman had a less permanent interest in the property and would secure all the profit he could. The Commissioners of the Forfeited Estates continued this risky system, but they did make some endeavour to restock the woods with natural regrowth, by building a wall to keep out crofters' beasts and wandering deer. The Wood at this time covered about 2,000 acres.

Early in the nineteenth century the Robertsons, who by then had regained control, sold the whole Wood to a

PLATE 26
Allean Forest beside Loch Tummel in Perthshire, looking eastwards from the southern shore.

PLATE 27
Loch Tay and Drummond Hill Forest, seen from Kenmore, west of Aberfeldy. The far snow-tipped peak is Ben Lawers.

timber company from the south. This concern built a system of canals within the Wood, at three different levels linked by steep sluices, and along these canals the felled logs were conveyed down to Loch Rannoch. There they were built into rafts and floated to the Tummel; they next travelled downstream, sometimes as single logs and sometimes in rafts, all the way to Perth, whence they were rafted down the Tay to Dundee. The intention was to clear all merchantable timber from the Black Wood, but the company failed after a few years and thereafter the Wood owed its survival to its remoteness. In 1857 the Robertsons sold it to the Wentworth family, who fenced it in as a deer park; this, of course, ensured that virtually all young seedlings were browsed down. The Wood was scheduled for felling in 1918, but was saved by the Armistice. In the 1939–45 war it was less fortunate, and the Canadian Forestry Corps cleared out all the good timber.

From the early eighteenth century onwards there had been a local demand for Rannoch pine on a lesser scale, involving the "creaming off" of all the better stems. At one time there was a sawmill at Dall, driven by water power. "Rannoch splints" or fragments of resinous pine-wood, were for long sold at country fairs to serve as candles or torches; they were burnt in a stand called "a puir mon"—a name derived from the old link-bearer of the baronial hall. Charcoal burning, to provide fuel for the smelting of iron ores, was practised on a large scale until the late eighteenth century; both birch and pine were used.

When acquired by the Forestry Commission in 1947, the Black Wood of Rannoch consisted mainly of over-aged trees rejected by successive timber seekers; there was far too little young growth, and natural regeneration had become sparse owing to the deterioration of the soil as non-forest conditions crept in. Part of the wood is now being restocked by replanting with pines raised from true Rannoch stock, while over another part experiments are in train to encourage natural regeneration through self-sown seed. Proper protection against livestock, deer, and fires is now provided.

Several interesting natural forms or races of Scots pine have been identified by foresters and botanists at Rannoch. The variety *horizontalis* has level branches and its crown assumes an umbrella-like form with age; it sheds its lower branches well, leaving a clean trunk of good timber form. The *ascensa* form has stout branches that follow the upward course of the trunk, while in the rare *fastigiata* form many small branches run up close to the trunk to give a tree like a Lombardy poplar. Other strange types are *pyramidalis* with a conical crown, and *pendula* with drooping branches. In the *condensata* form there is hardly any true tree trunk, but several large branches trend upwards and fuse together to produce a fluted stem of very bad timber form; this kind is common, for the plain reason that, like the other freaks, it was always rejected by the timber fellers. The curiosities comprise "the rugged Caledonian pine" of artists and poets, but are hardly fair samples of our native stock.

The birchwoods of the Tummel and Rannoch straths, which run up as high as 1,250 feet, are particularly fine, showing many vigorous trees with stout clean boles. For many years they have been grazed by sheep, which have reduced some areas to scrub by biting back and distorting seedlings, especially in snowy winters; but elsewhere good straight saplings are growing away.

Loch Tay and Breadalbane—*Plate 27*

From Rannoch we drop back to Ballinluig, to follow the course of the main River Tay upstream to Aberfeldy, passing several scattered plantations of spruce and pine, including those of the Grandtully Castle estate. Above the stone-built town of Aberfeldy lie the Falls of Moness, and the birchwoods that grow around them are praised in Burns' well-known poem and song: *The Birks of Aberfeldy.*

At Weem, just north of Aberfeldy, lies the Castle Menzies estate, with its fine old Scots baronial building. Its policies hold many grand specimen trees, and once boasted a sycamore, eighty feet in height, which had a girth of eighteen feet, and a volume of 1,000 hoppus feet. Close to Kenmore, six miles west of Aberfeldy, lie the extensive policies and plantations of the Taymouth Castle estate, which is oddly named inasmuch as it lies not at the mouth of the Tay, but at the point where that river runs out from Loch Tay to *start* its course to the

sea. Taymouth Castle has a recorded history running back to 1580, but the present enormous building, now an hotel, is mainly the work of the second Marquis of Breadalbane, and was constructed early in the nineteenth century. At that time the Breadalbane lands extended for over 100 miles, from Strathtay westwards to the Atlantic Ocean.

Just north of Kenmore, the big Drummond Hill Forest reaches over the long hill of that name, which rises from Loch Tay to an elevation of 1,500 feet. The southern slopes of this hill have the distinction of having carried one of the oldest known planted woodlands in Scotland. Between 1582 and 1631 Sir Duncan Campbell, known as Black Duncan of the Seven Castles, planted much of it with oak, birch, and Scots pine. Subsequent extensions and replantings eventually clothed the slopes with larch, pine and spruce, and smaller areas of oak, beech, and even sweet chestnut. But during the 1914–18 war the plantations were swept away, and in 1922 the cleared ground was transferred to the Commission for replanting. Among the fine trees felled at this period was a European larch reputed the largest ever grown in Scotland; aged 150 years, it reached 111 feet in height, girthed 18 feet and contained some 760 hoppus feet of timber (overbark measure).

Replanting since 1922 has been carried out largely with European larch, with Scots pine at the upper levels and Norway spruce in damp places. A forest road has been built right round the hill to aid the extraction of the large quantities of poles and timber obtained from thinnings. Drummond Hill is again a thriving source of useful timber and its great sweeps of green foliage add grandeur to the views of Loch Tay. Woods on the hill itself cover 2,500 acres, being four miles long by one mile wide; there are outlying, younger plantations at Borland, farther west, around Weem to the east, and also near Remony on the south side of Loch Tay. Spruces figure largely in these outlying woods. The total extent of the forest is 6,900 acres (over eleven square miles) and of this 4,900 acres ranks as tree-growing land.

Behind Drummond Hill runs Glen Lyon, winding down from the west for thirty-five miles and often called "the longest glen in Scotland". Near its lower end lies the village of Fortingall, and within its kirkyard stand the remains of that amazing old tree, the Fortingall Yew. There are conflicting records of its size in its prime, but the traveller Pennant assures us that in 1771 its decaying trunk was fifty-six feet round, which is a record for any known British tree. Its exact age can never be ascertained now that its heart has gone, but there is nothing improbable about the estimates of 3,000 years, based on the narrow annual rings and slow outward growth of venerable yews, that have sometimes been put forward. Close to Fortingall are the remains of a Roman camp, and a curious old legend declares that Pontius Pilate was born here, while his father was on a mission from the

PLATE 28
The eastward view from St. Fillans Forest, close to Crieff, over the rolling wooded hills of Strath Earn.

Emperor Caesar Augustus to the Scottish king Metellanus. Higher up Glen Lyon there are considerable plantations around Glenlyon House and Meggernie Castle.

Travelling westwards from Kenmore up Loch Tay, we find its shores sparsely wooded. Apart from the few new Commission plantations, there is little but patches of scrubby birch all the way to Killin. Loch Tay is sixteen miles long and one mile wide, and on its northern side Ben Lawers rises to 3,984 feet; this lofty hill is famous among botanists as the haunt for rare alpine plants surviving from the great Ice Age.

Away up Glen Dochart, some ten miles above Killin, the Commission has recently established its Glen Dochart Forest, on the slopes of Ben More and Stobinian. Much of its 14,000 acres is high mountain land and only

3,000 acres are being planted with spruce and pine. Further on still, beyond the road and rail junction of Crianlarich, lies Glen Orchy Forest, partly in Perthshire and partly in Argyll. This is best seen from the main road through Tyndrum to Bridge of Orchy. It is one of the Commission's largest new developments, involving 10,000 acres in all, of which 7,000 are plantable. Large areas are already being ploughed and planted with Sitka spruce and Lodgepole pine.

Strath Earn—*Plates 28 and 29*

Turning south at Killin we leave Loch Tay to travel through the narrow and rocky defile of Glen Ogle to Lochearnhead, at the western or upper end of Loch Earn. There we turn east towards Perth, and follow the north shore of the loch. There are fine views across the water to Ben Vorlich, which with its 3,224 feet forms the highest south-easterly bastion of the Grampians. Both sides of Loch Earn are clothed in broadleaved woodland, though much is little better than scrub; oak, birch, and alder are here the prevailing trees, and it is apparent that we have left the Highland fastnesses of birch and pine for milder lowland country. This softer character of the woodland continues right down the Earn to the outskirts of Perth, and appears also in the lower reaches of Glen Almond to the north. But it is much diversified by plantings of conifers—larch, pine, spruce, and Douglas fir—on the many well-tended estates and the occasional national forests.

Noteworthy estate woodlands along the course of the Earn are those of Dalchonzie, between St. Fillans and Comrie, Ochtertyre between Comrie and Crieff,

Drummond Castle south-west of Crieff, Abercairney east of that town, and Gask and Dupplin Castle between Crieff and Perth. In Glen Almond lie Glenalmond House, Logiealmond, and Lynedoch, all rich in plantations and fine policy trees. The Monzie estate near Crieff possesses Scotland's stoutest European larch, which is 18 feet 3 inches round and 108 feet tall.

St. Fillans Forest lies around the village of that name at the foot of Loch Earn, and extends to 4,000 acres, of which 3,000 acres are plantable. All its lands have been acquired since 1951, and most lie on remarkably steep slopes running down to Loch Earn or to the strath below it. Some were cleared woodland, others bare hill, when taken over; replanting with larch, pine, spruce, and Douglas fir is now completed.

Keillour Forest, which stands north of the main road

PLATE 29
Tree planters at work on the steep braes of St. Fillans Forest, central Perthshire.

PLATE 30
Ben Vorlich and Loch Earn, close to Balquhidder Forest, Perthshire.

between Crieff and Perth, is an older-established one. It dates from 1937, and most of its woods of spruce and pine are at the thinning stage. Keillour covers 2,000 acres, and occupies the long ridge that parts Strath Earn from Glen Almond. This region is notable for its remains of Roman occupation; a road, a camp and a signal station have all been identified near the forest.

Balquhidder and Strathyre—*Plates 30 to 33*

If you take the main Stirling road from Lochearnhead, a westward turn near Kingshouse soon leads to the old hamlet and kirk of Balquhidder, just above Loch Voil. That famous outlaw Rob Roy once farmed the lonely steading of Inverlochlarig at the head of Glen Voil, and died there in 1734. Now he sleeps peacefully in the

kirkyard beside his wife and their two sons Coll and Robert. One of the gravestones bears the arms of the Clan Macgregor—a pine tree torn up by the roots and a crown pierced by a sword—symbols of outlawry and disregarded royal descent. Above the kirk, on the Braes of Balquhidder, grow the young sprucewoods of the Balquhidder Forest, which rise to 1,700 feet above sea level and cover 2,000 acres. The far side of this peaceful strath holds woods of oak, birch, and hazel, around Stronvar.

Strathyre Forest lies along the beautiful valley of that name, from Kingshouse, down past Strathyre village and the shores of Loch Lubnaig to the Pass of Leny. The main road from Callander to Oban runs through it, and affords wonderful views of the plantations running high

E

55

PLATE 31
Looking north from Ben Ledi over Loch Lubnaig and Strathyre Forest towards Beinn Each.

up the foothills of Ben Vorlich on the east and Ben Ledi on the west. Three kinds of tree have been planted here since afforestation began in 1930, and each has been placed according to the vegetation that previously prevailed: pines have been set amid heather, larches among bracken, and spruces where grasses or rushes once grew strongly. The result is a multi-coloured pattern broken by the natural character of the hills, which accords well with the grand scenic framework of loch, crag, and snow-capped peak. Trees of all three kinds, so skilfully placed, have thriven well, and the thinning out of the plantations began when many were only sixteen years old. This meant a big call for labour, and to help meet this a group of smallholdings was built north of the village,

and a group of wooden houses set up on the far side of Loch Lubnaig; these particular houses were brought from Sweden in pre-fabricated sections, but elsewhere in Scotland home-grown timber has been used with equal effect. Strathyre Forest extends to 9,000 acres, of which 6,500 rank as tree-growing ground; the rest lies too high or is too rocky and steep. Strathyre is the home of the tallest Scots pine currently standing in Scotland, a tree 116 feet high by 7 feet in girth.

Just east of Strathyre Forest, but still on the shores of Loch Lubnaig, is the Ardchullarie Estate. Its name signifies "the high resort of the king", for here there was once a royal hunting lodge of the Scottish kings. They hunted the deer of Glenartney Forest, which lies over the hills to the east. At the foot of the loch the strath narrows abruptly into the Pass of Leny, and the conifer plantations are succeeded by the softer outlines of oak and birch, alder, elm and willow; here we cross the Highland Line into a kinder countryside.

Callander, Doune, and Flanders Moss

From Callander down to Doune and Dunblane the famous Braes o' Doune present a beautiful blending of farmland and forest, with fine woods of oak, beech, sycamore and the more ornamental conifers around the great houses, rivalling the utilitarian plantations of larch, spruce, and pine on the poorer uplands. From Callander all the way to Bridge of Allan both road and railway are bordered by continuous trees and woodland. Notable forestry estates in this favoured, south-facing region are those of Leny, Lanrick Castle, Doune Lodge, Blair Drummond, and Keir. Oak coppices around Callander were once highly valued for tanbark; those in the Wood of Keir were cut over every 21 years for 317 years, from 1590 to 1907! At Blair Drummond there is Scotland's stoutest lime tree, 21 feet round and 95 feet tall, and a superb oak 20 feet 8 inches round and 115 feet high.

Just to the south, lowland peat makes its appearance, particularly in the three mosses known as Drip Moss, Blair Drummond Moss, and Flanders Moss, which all lie near the course of the River Forth, and almost at sea level. From time to time the trunks of great oaks and pines have been unearthed during the digging of the

PLATE 32
A flock of Blackfaced sheep above Loch Lubnaig, in the heart of Strathyre Forest, Perthshire.

Loch Voil, beside Balquhidder Forest.

peat—relics of a great forest that grew on mineral soil in prehistoric times before the soft, sour peat began to accumulate. Around the year 1800, Lord Kames, the proprietor of the Blair Drummond Estate, reclaimed much of this fertile mineral substratum for agriculture by the simple expedient of stripping the peat and tipping it, with the aid of canals, into the Forth, so that it was carried down to the sea.

Torrie Forest, around Callander, now covers 2,100 acres. Part lies on the peaty moors along the road toward Thornhill, while other parts comprise former woodlands, some on the braes east of Callander town, others along the road west towards Loch Venachar and the Trossachs. Since 1949, afforestation with spruces, pines, and larches, has advanced steadily.

The Ochil Hills

Perthshire runs right down to the Forth on the outskirts of Stirling, but from the Bridge of Allan we turn north-east to follow Strath Allan in the direction of Perth. Around Dunblane lie woods of wych elm and oak, but as the road and railway climb the strath these give way to shelterbelts of conifers sparsely outlining upland pastures. At Gleneagles the crest of the rise is reached, high on the flanks of the Ochil Hills. Hidden away on the south side of the Ochils, but still within Perthshire, is Glendevon Forest, which takes its name from the village of Glendevon, though it also extends to neighbouring Glen Dye. Established in 1938, it comprises 2,200 acres, including 1,800 of sprucewoods and 400 of grazings.

5. Fife, Kinross and Clackmannan

Map: page 48

The hilly peninsula of Fife, set betwixt the Firth of Tay and the Firth of Forth, carries a density of woodland above the average for Scotland. Most of this lies evenly dispersed on the numerous well-tended private estates; the Forestry Commission has only a small share in developments, though some of its properties are of unusual interest.

Tayside and the Howe of Fife

Starting from Perth we approach the borders of Fife at Abernethy, a village which still preserves an ancient Pictish round tower or broch. Here the north-eastern end of the Ochils forms a broken range of foothills, that carries a fair sprinkling of plantations. On the crest of these hills, midway between Abernethy and Auchtermuchty, and partly in Perthshire and partly in Fife, stands Pitmedden Forest. Planting began here in 1939, and the young woods now extend to 2,100 acres. The chief trees used are Scots and Corsican pines, Sitka spruce, and Japanese larch. This larch has grown very rapidly—a reflection perhaps of the genial climate of this sunny sea-girt land—and some stands were ready for thinning only twelve years after they were planted.

Travelling on into Fife, we reach the little town of Newburgh with its ancient abbey. In the Middle Ages the monks of Newburgh and Lindores held extensive rights over forests in Perthshire, as far afield as Glenorchy. North-east of Newburgh the Ochil ridge rises to 936 feet high on Norman's Law, a landmark overlooking the Firth of Tay, and between that hill and Balmerino a fringe of woods runs for four miles along the shore. The Wormit and St. Fort estates, close to the Tay railway bridge, hold 400 acres of well-managed woods, largely of conifers, but with some good oak, beech, sycamore, ash, and wych elm.

South of the Ochil foothills lies the Howe of Fife, a fertile, sunny hollow amid encircling hills, which yields rich crops of grain and sugar beet. It includes, around Ladybank, some contrasting patches of poor and sterile soils lying low down in the basin of the River Eden, which have proved suitable only for afforestation. In 1923 much of this ground, some of it cleared woodland and some moorland, was taken in hand for tree-planting, to form the new Edensmuir Forest, which now occupies 2,000 acres. Historical records show that in the 12th century these lands belonged to Lindores Abbey. The Torloisk section, which has associations with Falkland Palace, was acquired later; it consists of patches of old woodland on the Clatto Hills, over towards Leven. The older woods are being thinned, and trees removed find a ready market as pitprops in the Fife coalfield just to the south.

Tentsmuir

From Ladybank we may follow road and railway north-east through the market town of Cupar, to the little village of Leuchars, well-known for its exquisite old Norman church and its aerodrome. Leuchars is also the railway junction for St. Andrews, world famous as an ancient seat of learning and the home of Royal and Ancient golf. Nearby, right at the north-eastern tip of the Fife peninsula, stands the remarkable forest called Tentsmuir. The whole shoulder of land between the Tay and the North Sea is really a great flat sea beach, raised just above the level of tides but consisting of little more than blown sand. However, most of this has been "fixed" by vegetation, and prior to afforestation it carried heather and was used as a grouse moor. The seaward fringe of sand dunes is still shifting, though it carries much marram grass, but it serves to shield the inland portions from encroaching sands. These sands are apparently brought down the firth by the Tay, and are gradually extending the land eastwards. The planting of Tentsmuir Forest began in 1922, and the area involved is now 4,000 acres, of which 3,600 are under trees. Only two kinds have been used in quantity, namely the Scots and Corsican pines. Both are well suited to the sandy soil, the low rainfall, and the hot sunshine of this curious corner of Scotland, but the Corsican pine gives the higher yield of timber. The land is very flat, nowhere rising more than thirty feet above the level of the sea, and it is divided up by a gridwork of straight rides, to give easy access and to help stop any fires spreading. A fire look-out tower overlooks the whole. Thinnings have long been in progress at Tentsmuir and large quantities of poles and pit props are harvested each year.

PLATE 34   Sunlight through the sycamores. A spring view in the woods of Airthrey Castle, home of the new Stirling University.

The seashore at Tentsmuir attracts many rare sea-birds and waders, and the Morton Lochs nearby, where many kinds nest, form a Nature Conservancy Reserve. The Conservancy also looks after a stretch of sea coast, where other kinds of birds either nest, feed, or congregate during their migrations; the dune vegetation also holds high scientific interest and includes many rare plants.

The south-eastern corner of Fife has only a thin sprinkling of woodland, and from St. Andrews right round to Leven there is no single large wood. Occasional shelterbelts of conifers stud the hills, and several of the estates have good stands of beech and other broadleaved trees, which enjoy the sunny maritime climate of this pleasant region. Near Kirkcaldy, larger sweeps of woodland provide an attractive foil to industry; the Raith estate just east of that town is noted for its forestry activities.

Wooden Fishing Craft

The little harbour of Anstruther in the East Neuk of Fife has one of the several small shipyards that still build wooden fishing craft. Scots-grown oak is always chosen for the frames of the little drifters that have to face fierce buffeting from the North Sea gales. The planking of the hull is always of home-grown larch, of the quality aptly described as "boat-skin". In each case a natural curvature of the timber is used to gain extra strength; with the oak it takes the form of bends or knees where branches curve or leave the main trunk; in the larch it is the "sweep" given to the base of the growing stem by the prevailing wind. Selected poles of Douglas fir, still known in the trade by its old name of "Oregon pine", are used for the masts; these are usually imported, though comparable stuff is now raised in Scotland. In 1957 a large wooden "liner", or fish carrier to bring in the catches of trawlers, nearly 100 feet long, was built of home grown timber at Anstruther.

Pit Props for the Coalfield

Amid the industrial towns of the Fife coalfield near the Firth of Forth, a large Commission forest, established on cleared woodland, poor hill ground, and even here and there on old spoil heaps, provides a veil of pleasant green foliage. Scots pine and the spruces are the main trees grown, and thinnings find a market as pit props in the mines nearby. This forest, Blairadam, is centred on Cowdenbeath, but draws its name from the estate of Blairadam, which was designed and built as his private residence by one of the Adam brothers of architectural and political fame. It comprises in all some 3,400 acres of land. The oldest and largest block lies west of the mining town of Kelty, in the direction of the Cleish Hills: the plantations here date from 1927; they are

largely of Scots pine and the spruces, and have been undergoing thinning for several years. Part of this block falls in Kinross-shire, and looks north towards Loch Leven and Kinross; it is plainly in view from the main road and railway that link Perth with Edinburgh. Other blocks of woods stand on Benarty Hill, between Kelty and Loch Leven, around the new town of Glenrothes, and in the triangle of land between Cowdenbeath, Dunfermline, and Burntisland.

The Scottish coal mines now meet all their needs of pit props and other mining timber from the country's own woods. This represents a great change from the pre-war situation, when the larger proportion was imported from Scandinavia. Scots-grown timber has shown itself equal in working properties and strength to that from overseas, particularly as foresters now recognise the need to supply well-seasoned and properly trimmed props, which have had their bark removed. The miner, working under difficult conditions underground, appreciates a well prepared prop for several reasons; it is lighter than an unseasoned one, yet at the same time stronger, and being free from snags is less likely to cause chance injuries. Though steel props are also employed, the wooden ones still hold an important place; they are cut into a considerable range of sizes to suit the various depths of seams and heights of working galleries. Sawn hardwood timber is also used to build up stout pillars and to serve as caps or "crown trees", for the vertical pit props.

Around Aberdour and Inverkeithing a good deal of broadleaved woodland flourishes under the mild conditions induced by the southward slope towards the Firth of Forth. The native oak, ash, and wych elm all thrive here, and there is much planted beech and sycamore. This broadleaved character is continued in the numerous scattered woods that lie farther west between Dunfermline, Dollar, and Alloa; and also in those to the north, near Rumbling Bridge. But many good stands have vanished in past fellings, and the land left idle has been colonised by the aggressive but less valuable birch. The picturesque fringe of oak hedgerow trees along the low ground bordering the Firth of Forth, between Kincardine and North Queensferry, well shows the strong moulding effect of the south-west wind, intensified here by the salt whipped off the sea water.

Clackmannan, Devilla and Tulliallan Nursery

On the borders of Fife and Clackmannan the large Devilla Forest includes a big main block, reaching for three miles from the Dunfermline-Alloa road to the Dunfermline-Kincardine road. There are outlying portions near Culross, Dollar, and Alva, and the total extent is 3,700 acres. Planting began here in 1929, but much of the ground has been acquired more recently and so carries younger plantations. Scots pine is the principal tree in the older woods, but spruces and larches are also planted.

It was at Devilla Forest that, about 1946, important experiments were made in the raising of seedling trees in nurseries formed on old heathland or woodland soils, rather than on agricultural land. Such ground comes closer to that normally found in a forest than does old arable soil, but the main practical advantage to the forester is its relative freedom from weeds. Given a well-drained and workable soil, he can enrich it with humus and chemical fertilisers to the extent he requires. By using a weed-free form of humus—in this case spent hops from the Alloa breweries—rather than farmyard manure with its inevitable content of weed seeds, he avoids both weed competition and the high cost of weeding. Consequently he can raise in one year a seedling that, under other conditions, would need two years to reach the same size, and a big economy results. Such methods, developed at Devilla, have now been adopted at most forest tree nurseries in Scotland. This small, seven-acre nursery has produced, in one season, as many as 8 million seedling trees!

Tulliallan Forest Nursery, which draws its name from the Tulliallan Castle estate, is situated two miles east of Kincardine-on-Forth, on either side of the main road to Dunfermline. It covers 112 acres, and has been worked ever since 1921, as the main source of supply of young trees for planting in the *West* of Scotland. This site was chosen because of its mild climate, moderate rainfall, easily worked soil, and ample labour supply; for it is found easier to raise young trees under such conditions than under the heavy rainfall found farther west, which hampers outdoor work but encourages weed growth. Several score workers are employed here, many being lads, women and girls, for much nursery work is of a light character. Houses and smallholdings have been provided for about twenty-five workers, and others come from the towns of Culross, Kincardine, and Clackmannan nearby. The Alloa breweries are the source of the spent hops required in large quantities as an organic manure.

At Tulliallan there is a seed extraction station, to which cones, gathered in autumn from good stands of trees, are sent from all over Scotland. Each batch of cones is carefully heated until their scales dry and expand, allowing the precious seeds to fall out; the cones are shaken up in wire drums to assist this process; the seeds fall through the wire mesh, and are then collected. At this stage each seed has a little wing attached, and this is next removed by a de-winging machine, so that the seed becomes easier to handle. It is then stored in refrigerated chambers under carefully controlled conditions of temperature and moisture until it is needed for sowing. Some kinds of seed only keep their germinative power until the next spring, but others can be kept in cold storage for several years, if so required, and this evens out the annual variations in the size of every crop of seed.

Much of the tiny county of Clackmannan comprises a coalfield, but nevertheless several large woods survive around Alloa, under the shadow of the steep south face of the Ochil Hills. As we leave the Fife peninsula for Stirling we may note the broadleaved woods, with much wych elm, that clothe the braes nearby.

6. Edinburgh and the Lothians

Map: page 47

From Stirling we follow the southern shore of the Firth of Forth eastwards, and while still in Stirlingshire reach the great port of Grangemouth, where the old Forth and Clyde Canal enters the sea at the mouth of the River Carron. Besides being a centre of industry and oil refining, Grangemouth is Scotland's principal port for timber imports. Most of this material comes over from Scandinavia and the Baltic in small craft, which can sail well up the rivers at either end of their run. From Grangemouth it is readily distributed, by road or rail, to the main industrial belt of mid-Scotland.

The importation of timber from the North of Europe is a large and old-established trade which might well puzzle an impartial economist. There is land enough in Scotland to grow all the timber that any foreseeable population is likely to consume, but the home-grown merchants have to face competition from importers who cheerfully bear the cost of transport from forests thousands of miles away. A large part of the cost of timber to the consumer consists of transport charges—from the tree stump to the sawmill, then to the port of shipment, then across the water and finally from the home port to his factory door. The Scandinavian producers make use of firm frozen ground in winter, and of floating down their great rivers in spring, to get their logs to mills well placed beside a seaport; and sea freight was, in the past, so cheap that they could undercut our home producers. Now rising sea freight charges have helped home-grown pitwood to take its rightful place as the only timber in Scottish mines; and as time goes on and our expanding forests become more mature, they will supply a growing share of the sawn timber that is cut from the larger trees.

The importers have long been able to offer selected grades of timber—albeit at higher prices—because their big volume of trade made it easy to sort out whatever came through their mills. Now a similar scheme of grading has been adopted in Scotland. Intrinsically, the imported material is much the same as the home-grown, being either "redwood" from Scots pine, or "whitewood" from Norway spruce. That which comes from the far north is more slowly grown and closer-textured—which is an advantage in fine joiner's work, though seldom otherwise. Merits claimed for slow-grown timber on the grounds of greater durability have not

stood the tests of the scientists' laboratories, nor those of the user's experience. Strength depends on wood density and is highest in timber from trees having a *moderate* rate of growth. Both very fast-grown and very slow-grown timbers lack high strength, but on average the home-grown material matches that imported.

The Lothians West of the Pentlands

Following the coast round past Blackness Castle, we come to the great estate of Hopetoun House, which enjoys both a warm and sheltered situation and a fertile soil. Its policies include an exceptionally rich collection of rare specimen trees, and are laid out in the grand manner; they include a grand specimen of the native ash, 105 feet high and the tallest in Scotland. Beyond Queensferry lies another great estate, that of Dalmeny House, which includes a large expanse under timber, with much tall beech, oak, and sycamore. The public footpath that follows the coastline round from Queensferry, past the Forth Bridge and Hound Point, to Cramond on the outskirts of Edinburgh, is fringed with broadleaved trees. The close association of woodland with salt water is rare in Britain, but here it is aided by shelter from the south-west winds.

Just inland from these maritime properties lies a narrow fringe of fertile lowland, adjoining the main road and railway from Linlithgow to Edinburgh, where each country mansion has its sheltering screen of broadleaved trees—largely beech and sycamore, but with some wych elm, oak, and ash. The general aspect of the country here resembles that of an English Midland shire. But go just a few miles inland, to the higher ground around Bathgate, dotted with pit heaps and the weird red shale tips or "bings" produced by the shale oil industry, and the northerly nature of the country begins to assert itself. The soils derived from the coal-bearing rocks are poor and ill-drained, and clad in peat over considerable areas. Efforts have been made in the past to protect the better ground with shelterbelts, for one of the chief difficulties for the farmer is the fury of the south-westerly gales that sweep across this narrow, and relatively low, "waist" of Scotland between Clyde and Forth. But many such belts have been felled or have become neglected.

Nevertheless they enable agriculture to be sustained at several points to elevations exceeding 800 feet. The railway line from Edinburgh, past the high Cobbinshaw Reservoir, to Carstairs Junction, runs for many miles through this marginal farming zone.

The struggle to maintain arable land eventually gives out on the flanks of the Pentland Hills, between 800 and 1,000 feet above sea level. The Pentlands, with their grand scenery, are now closely grazed by sheep, and therefore carry no tree cover. But the odd birches, rowans, willows, and juniper bushes down in their cleughs show that at one time this was wooded country. Their lower slopes have provided a good testing ground for shelterbelts, and researches carried out by Dr. J. M. Caborn of the Forestry Department of Edinburgh University have added to our knowledge of the influence of trees on the winds. Only conifers—usually Scots pine, Sitka spruce, and European larch—thrive under the exposed conditions found here. At one time shelter blocks—into the lee of which sheep may draw when blizzards sweep the hills—were grown as high up as 1,600 feet close to Scald Law, which at 1,898 feet is the highest point on the Pentlands; none of these now remain.

In 1953 the Forestry Commission started the Selm Muir Forest on the Pentland flanks east of West Calder. This consists largely of narrow belts and small blocks where the raising of such hardy trees as lodgepole pine and Sitka spruce, on ground prepared by ploughing, will afford valuable shelter to pastoral farms. Recently small woods between Bathgate and Broxburn, due for replanting, have come under the Commission's care, while farther west two large expanses of poor peaty moorland have been acquired for planting up; one of these lies in West Lothian, between Whitburn and Fauldhouse, the other in Stirlingshire between Slamannan and the Black Loch. In all, 1,700 acres of land are involved; some of the woods will give much-needed shelter to Livingston New Town, which is now springing up in their midst, besides relieving its rather bleak surroundings.

Edinburgh

The city of Edinburgh has an established place in Scottish forestry as a centre of Forestry Commission research, the home of the Royal Scottish Forestry Society and the Scottish Woodland Owners Association, and the seat of a university having a long-established forestry department. It is also the centre of land management and legal transactions for many estates scattered throughout the whole country. The Royal Botanic Garden at Inverleith maintains a good collection of forest trees representative of all the temperate forests of the world, and has a big herbarium that aids their identification and further study.

At the Bush Estate, owned by the University and situated near Milton Bridge some eight miles south of the city, near the road to Penicuik, the Commission's Research Branch maintains experimental nurseries. A modern research station will open here in 1970.

Edinburgh is also the centre of a long-established trade in the raising of forest and ornamental trees from seed in nursery gardens. Early in the eighteenth century William Boutcher, who had a nursery at Comely Bank, wrote a long textbook giving detailed instructions for raising the principal kinds, and much of what he said is still followed today. The tree raising tradition has been continued by other firms, including Messrs. Dicksons, who raise large quantities of forest and ornamental trees at Craigmillar, south of the city.

Being a centre of varied trades and crafts, Edinburgh is a big timber-consuming centre. Large quantities of foreign timber are landed at Leith, while much home-grown stuff is brought in by road and rail. A number of modern saw-mills are in operation, while there are also coopers who make oaken vats and barrels for the large brewery trade, and a small number of highly skilled decorative and artistic wood carvers.

With so much interest evident in trees from seed to timber, and in the administrative, scientific, and educational sides of forestry, one would expect to find a city ornamented by fine trees. But in this respect Edinburgh proves disappointing. It is not a congenial home for them. A combination of the smoky atmosphere that originated its name of Auld Reekie, the fierce winds that smite it alternately from east and west, and a sterile subsoil, leads to indifferent growth. Ample space for parks has been provided in its lay-out—both that of the famous New Town and in more recent extensions, but the trees so diligently planted appear ungrateful. They live, but scarcely grow. The kind that is most characteristic of the city—as the plane is characteristic of London—is the wych or Scots elm, *Ulmus glabra;* it takes little harm from smoke, resists wind and tolerates poor soil; but it never reaches a great size nor does it equal here its appearance amid the cleaner surroundings of the Highland glens or the dales of the Southern Uplands.

However, hidden amid the stones of Edinburgh lie some remarkable sylvan nooks, especially along the deep gorge of the Water of Leith. The Queen's Park around Arthur's Seat once ranked as a forest or royal hunting ground, but it has been grazed for sheep for so long that nowadays nothing less tough than a gorse bush survives. Conifers are rare in the city, for the smoke discourages them, but there are shelterbelts farther out, particularly near Dreghorn on the northern face of the Pentland Hills.

Eastern Midlothian and Dalkeith

That portion of Midlothian which lies east of the Pentlands holds—or at least held—a close network of shelterbelts designed to protect the arable land of great estates from the elements. The ground rises quickly from the coast, on either side of the valleys of the Rivers North Esk and South Esk, towards the moorland plateau that culminates in the sheep pastures of the Pentland, the Moorfoot and the Lammermuir Hills. By well-planned shelter plantings the proprietors of the eighteenth and nineteenth centuries found that they could maintain profitable mixed farming up to the level of 800, or locally 1,000 feet. Unfortunately the development of the Midlothian coalfield, the spread of suburbs and industrial townships, and wartime fellings have broken up the fine panorama of big, well timbered estates, though active replanting and restoration are now evident.

The Dalkeith estates of the Duke of Buccleuch present a fine example of well-managed woodland, with broadleaved trees as their main crop. They extend to nearly 500 acres, and their plan of management provides for one-third being kept under oak, one-third under beech and sycamore, and one-third under larch and other conifers. The aim is to get a regular succession of age-classes through the woods, so that as one block is felled another is being replanted; the area felled each year does not exceed ten acres, so there are never any large gaps in the woods. Much of the timber cut is converted on the estate's own sawmill, the balance being sold to timber merchants. It is estimated that the broadleaved crops have a current annual increment of more than 50 hoppus feet per acre, and it is hoped to increase this by prudent management; the present figure is low by comparison with the speed of growth of conifers, but it must be remembered that mature broadleaved timbers are commonly worth twice as much per unit of volume. These Dalkeith woods have been under planned management since 1906, and in every year since then one or more sections have been cleared and replanted.

The Forestry Commission maintains some small woods south of Bonnyrigg, close to the Dalhousie Burn. Right at the head of the South Esk, not far from Leadburn, there is a big coniferous plantation close to the Glad-house Reservoir.

This portion of the Lothians has a landscape that is largely man-made, as evidenced by the rectangular lay-out of roads and fields. Few traces of natural woodlands remain, save along the steep banks of winding streams like the River Esk and its tributaries. Even the birch is largely an invader of land cleared of planted woods. A sycamore at Gilmerton, 106 feet high, is believed to be the tallest in Scotland.

East Lothian—*Plate 35*

The pleasant county of East Lothian is almost wholly agricultural in character. Its lowlands have fertile soils and one of the sunniest and driest climates in Scotland, but despite very intensive agriculture, including the growing of potatoes and market garden crops, they retain a fair quota of woodland. Only the bleak Lammermuirs, rising on the south to elevations around 1,700 feet, are treeless.

We will first look at the beautiful coastal fringe which faces in turn west up the Firth of Forth, north over to Fife, and east to the open expanse of the North Sea; much of it can be glimpsed from the main railway line from Edinburgh to Berwick-on-Tweed and the South, which makes a broad sweep into this level shoulder of land.

Gosford Shelterbelt

Almost on the coast, between Longniddry and Aberlady, is the big Gosford Estate owned by the Earl of Wemyss, which includes 400 acres of woodlands. It is noteworthy for the two-mile-long shelterbelt that shields the park from the fierce westerly gales that sweep up the Forth. This belt of trees rises just behind the boundary wall which borders the main road to North Berwick, and for much of the way only the road divides it from the actual sea shore. The amazing thing about this belt is the way in which the wind has sheared off the twigs at the top of the trees, producing a great sloping surface gradually rising towards the east, which looks more like a hill than the top of a wood. Much of this effect is due to the salt content of the wind, which scorches delicate young buds and leads to one-sided growth.

The estate records show that the present mansion of Gosford House was built in 1796, and the coastal wall in 1800, the woods being planted at various dates from 1796 to 1807. Before this the lands were one vast and sandy rabbit warren, but protection from the wind has made possible their development into a fertile park. A mixture of trees was planted in the shelterbelts, but those now most prominent are sycamore, wych elm, Scots pine, and European larch; the two hardwoods show particularly good resistance to the salt-laden sea breezes. The trees beside the wall are only ten feet high, but those on the inland side of the belt reach fifty feet. The sheltered inland trees have each twice the volume of the exposed seaward trees, and the inland areas are growing timber at twice the rate of the seaward ones. This is an extreme case, but it does show how severe exposure reduces the speed of timber production.

Following the road along the coast, we pass the marshy bird sanctuary of Aberlady Bay, and beyond Gullane go past the Archerfield estate, which lies down towards the sea. Here there is an expanse of sand dunes which the Commission is now afforesting with pines, to check the

PLATE 35   Magnificent beech on the Yester Estate near Gifford in East Lothian, typical of the grand hardwoods grown in the fertile Lowlands.

inland drift of the sand. The three rocky islets of Fidra, Craigleith, and the Bass Rock, where the gannets nest each spring, rise sheer from the mouth of the Forth, while North Berwick Law stands like a sentinel over the flat coastal plain. Following the coast round eastwards, we come to the estate of Tyninghame, where the little River Tyne runs out into a broad sandy bay. Here the Earl of Haddington has over 900 acres of intensively managed woodlands, which include a high proportion of hardwoods. Some grand old beeches grow right down to the edge of the tidal water, on a substratum of almost pure sand. There are also crops of oak and sycamore, and some natural birch and alder. The conifers grown here include Scots pine, Norway spruce, and hybrid larch.

A Planting Laird

Thomas Hamilton, the Sixth Earl of Haddington, who flourished from 1680 to 1735, was an able and enthusiastic tree planter who left behind a valuable record of the practices current in his day. When this was first published, in the 1756 edition of *The Scots Gard'ner*, it bore the comprehensive title of *A Short Treatise on Forest Trees, Acquaticks, Ever-greens and Grass-seeds, by the Right Honourable the Late Earl of Haddington*; it has been re-issued in a scholarly edition prepared by Professor Anderson under the title of *Forest Trees* (Nelson, 1953), which preserves the charming style of printing current in that elegant age. The Sixth Earl, who took an active part in the politics of his day, resided a great deal in London, and probably gained many ideas from the methods used in southern nurseries. He introduced and raised successfully a large number of trees and shrubs foreign to Scotland, including walnut, sweet chestnut, horse chestnut, hornbeam, cork oak, sweet bay, and cherry laurel. He planted the great Binning Wood, of 300 acres, which survived until 1944 and was then felled to meet war needs, yielding over half a million hoppus feet of prime timber; it has since been replanted. Some of his grand old beech avenues still stand.

Stenton and Whittingehame

Near the picturesque red-roofed village of East Linton, the Lammermuir Hills come close to the coast, and on their northern flanks the Forestry Commission is building up a rather scattered forest called, after the largest village in the district, Stenton. It comprises several separate blocks, largely of cleared woodland down in sheltered valleys, with a total area of 2,300 acres, and a proportion of broadleaved trees is used in the replanting work.

The estate of Whittingehame, famous as the seat of the family of Balfour, possesses a small arboretum which is now in the care of the Forestry Commission, and which includes a most remarkable tree. This is a "walking" or layering yew, with the odd habit of sending out branches that bend over, touch the ground, take root, and then send up fresh stems, so that the whole tree slowly advances outwards on a circular plan. This old yew has achieved remarkable dimensions: its trunk is eleven feet round, and the branches first strike the ground some 20 feet out from the centre, producing the effect of a natural summer house. After taking root, the branches continue to grow outwards for a further twenty feet, slowly rising to an upward direction; their total radius is over 76 feet and in order to encircle the tree it is necessary to walk 150 yards. The tree is 43 feet high. There is an old tradition, which may well be true, that it was beneath this tree that Bothwell and his fellow-conspirators plotted the murder of Darnley, the husband of Mary, Queen of Scots in 1566.

The Commission maintains seed orchards at Whittingehame, where it holds, in all, thirty acres. Farther west, and not far from Haddington town, there is a big cluster of woods around Gifford. The Commission's properties include Saltoun Big Wood, south of East Saltoun village, which lies on a fertile though heavy clay; much of the planting here is being done with broadleaved trees. Although it lies so closely in to industrial areas, Saltoun Forest is still the haunt of the shy roe deer.

The rest of the East Lothian woods consists of shelterbelts and blocks, often pitched surprisingly high up the north face of the Lammermuirs. Several touch the 1,000-foot contour, and near Lammer Law (1,753 feet and the highest of the range) one belt goes as high as 1,400 feet. These woods, mainly of Scots pine and larch, are grown purely to shelter the sheep in winter, or the marginal fields lower down; but they do suggest that there is no real altitudinal limit for forest growth in this easterly hill range.

The importance of the native wych or Scots elm in the three Lothian counties is noteworthy. It also persists along many hillside cleughs, and is a favourite tree for planting in the towns. Wych elm seems more frequent in the Lothian and Border counties than anywhere else in Scotland.

Two East Lothian estates hold record-breaking trees. A beech at Yester House, 142 feet high, is the tallest in Britain. An oak, *Quercus robur*, at Marchmount, 128 feet high, is likewise the tallest of its kind so far recorded anywhere in the British Isles.

PLATE 36—The infant River Forth at Aberfoyle, with Loch Ard Forest and Ben Lomond beyond; Queen Elizabeth Forest Park.

68

7. The Borders

Berwick, Peebles, Selkirk, Roxburgh and Dumfries

Map: page 47

This survey of the forests of southern Scotland takes us first down the east coast towards Berwick-upon-Tweed, and then up the great Tweed inland from mouth to source, diverging to explore its nothern tributaries. Returning downstream, we wander into the dales of the Yarrow, Teviot, and Jed Water, and then go west where the Esk, the Annan and the Nith flow down to meet the Solway Firth, near the town of Dumfries.

Berwickshire

The main road and railway from Edinburgh to Berwick-upon-Tweed run side by side, hugging the coast from Dunbar to Cockburnspath. There they turn inland, and climb up a long narrow glen to Grantshouse. For two miles their course is bordered by a thriving, privately-owned, plantation of larches, which regular travellers have watched developing over the years. From little trees set out on the braes they have grown to their present stage of a tall pole plantation, undergoing thinning to yield durable fencing material, rustic poles, and small saw-logs.

The Forestry Commission also has plantations scattered over this eastern shoulder of the Lammermuirs, but they are still young and hence not in the public eye; they form part of its Duns Forest.

Between the railway and the little fishing harbour of Eyemouth on the rocky coast lies the Ayton Castle estate, which has over 400 acres of well-managed woods. Broadleaved trees are found over about 160 acres, the main species being oak, ash, beech, elm, lime, and sycamore; the 240 acres of conifers are mainly Scots pine, with European larch, spruces, and Douglas fir playing a minor part. There are also extensive woodlands farther up the Ale Water, close to Press Castle and Coldingham.

From Berwick we turn inland and go westwards up the Tweed's most northern tributary, the Whiteadder Water. Around Chirnside lie several blocks of woodland dispersed among the closely farmed agricultural lands of the Merse. The market town of Duns, standing on a hill midway betwixt the dales of the Whiteadder and the Blackadder, is neighboured on the north by the extensive woodlands of the Duns Castle estate. These cover nearly 600 acres, and include plantations of Japanese larch, Sitka spruce, and Douglas fir. There are broadleaved woods of sycamore and ash, which renew themselves readily by means of self-sown seed; natural regeneration of silver firs is also found.

Duns gives its name to a Commission forest of 1,600 acres, scattered over a wide hinterland of Lammermuir dales. Some portions lie as far afield as Cockburnspath near the coast, and others around Abbey St. Bathans, while there is one block well up the hills some three miles west of Duns, and others in the remote fastnesses beyond Longformacus. Over twenty pieces of ground are included, and some plantings serve as shelter blocks for the sheep hirsels. Hardwoods are used for planting some of the valley woods, but those on the hill call for hardy pines and spruces.

Large groups of privately owned woodland lie on the foothills around Polwarth and Fogo. Thence we cross the broad and fertile plain of mid Berwickshire to Coldstream, a little town right on the Tweed, which marks the English Border. The estate called The Hirsel, close to Coldstream, has a large group of woodlands, and is noted for its exceptionally fine beeches. Several of these have been chosen as parent stocks for the Forestry Commission's collection of seed-producing strains, which are propagated by grafting in seed orchards.

Kelso and Bowmont

Following the Tweed upstream we enter Roxburghshire to reach Kelso, the principal market town for this rich farming region. Floors Castle, seat of the Duke of Roxburghe, which dates from Tudor times, has many fine specimen trees in its beautiful grounds. The forestry activities of the Floors estate embrace 1,500 acres, the largest block being that called Bowmont Forest, four miles south of Kelso. It stands in lonely country where the Kale Water flows quietly down from its remote source on Hungry Law in the Central Cheviots, fifteen miles away. There was an older, and far more extensive, Bowmont Forest in days gone by. The stream called the Bowmont Water, which flows through Kirk Yetholm, lies five miles further east. It rises on the Cheviot itself—that grand square bastion of the range, 2,676 feet high, which stands just on the English side of the Border.

The present Bowmont Forest extends to 600 acres, and was first planted in the years following 1815 to give employment to soldiers returning from the Napoleonic wars; some 2 million trees were put in, but those first crops have long ago reached maturity and been replaced by a second generation of trees. These consist largely of conifers, with good stands of Scots pine, Japanese larch, and Norway and Sitka spruces, thriving on a good sandstone soil in a region of kindly climate.

Bowmont Forest is famous among foresters—not only in Scotland but in other countries too—for a unique experiment on the thinning treatment of a coniferous crop. In 1930 the Forestry Commission's Research Branch, in co-operation with the estate, laid out a series of sixteen plots in a uniform stand of Norway spruce, then twenty years old. These sixteen plots were divided into four groups, arranged in such a way that any local differences in the ground would not affect the issue, and the groups have been treated ever since on different thinning régimes. Some are thinned heavily, others lightly. After twenty-five years of divergent treatment, quite remarkable differences were apparent, even to the non-professional observer, in the resultant crops. Once there were 3,000 trees to the acre in all the plots. In 1955 lightly thinned ones held 1,200 trees per acre, heavily thinned ones only 200. But although there were six times as many trees in the lightly thinned plots, there was only twice as much timber, which means that the individual trees were, on average, only one-third the size.

All the plots have grown to much the same height, and consequently the lightly-thinned plot presents the appearance of closely ranked long thin poles, while the heavily-thinned one looks like a mature forest of stout timber trees. It is hard to credit that it is not, by many years, the older of the two.

In growing to this state, it has yielded, in successive thinnings, so much material that the total volume produced by the two types, over the years, has been much the same. In fact, a slight advantage, about 10 per cent, rests with the heavily-thinned plots.

All this is valuable scientific knowledge for the forester, for it shows how he can influence the growth of his crops. The traditional school in Scotland has long favoured light thinnings, but the Bowmont plots show that heavy ones have great advantages; they have produced timber big enough for the sawmills far sooner than the others could do—and *that* large timber is worth more money for every unit of volume. Now that thinnings are sold at a profit, there is a sound financial advantage in the heavier thinning régime.

Leaving Kelso we go north-west towards Lauder, passing the extensive woodlands of the Mellerstain estate, which include much fine beech and Scots pine. Lauderdale is remarkable for the extensive system of coniferous shelterbelts that protect its big farms. They form peculiar rectangular patterns in the broad landscape and, in the region known as Lauder Common, run up to heights exceeding 1,000 feet.

Around Lauder stands Edgarhope Forest, named after a wood just north of the town. It covers 1,500 acres in ten separate portions. The smaller woods are of varied character, some being old policies and others shelter blocks, with others again on steep hill slopes. The Spottiswood portion, four miles east of Lauder, was once the park of a great house, now demolished. Planting began at Edgarhope in 1929, and has involved a variety of trees—oak and beech on the more fertile portions, and the Scots and lodgepole pines, Norway and Sitka spruces, and European larch elsewhere. The older plantations are now in the thinning stages.

Away to the north of Lauderdale the Lammermuirs stretch as a treeless sea of bents and heather, grazed by the hardy blackfaced sheep, for mile after roadless mile, and so our circuit of Berwickshire is completed.

Melrose to Peebles—*Plate 37*

Between Melrose and Peebles the Tweed and its northern tributaries touch on five counties, so we ignore the county borders in our exploration of Tweed's deep dale and the tree-covered slopes above it. In the Middle Ages, when the Abbeys of Melrose, Dryburgh, and Jedburgh flourished, their monks pastured great flocks of sheep in the wild country to the south, which was known as "Jed Forest" along the headwaters of the Jed Water, and as "Ettrick Forest", further west, up the dales of the Ale, Ettrick, and Yarrow Waters. Much of their income came from wool, which they exported profitably to the Continent; but the sheep, by their close grazing and browsing, gradually reduced the hills to treeless pasture. So the romantic ruins of the Borders provide a clue to the disappearance of tree cover from the countryside. Most of the woods we see along the Tweed today are the outcome of planting during the last two hundred years.

Prominent among the planting lairds was Sir Walter Scott, who lived beside the Tweed, first at Ashiesteel west of Galashiels and later at Abbotsford—the grand estate he created between Melrose and Selkirk. Scott wrote several papers on forestry, and it is to him that we owe the current practice of calling the native Scots pine, *Pinus sylvestris*, a *pine* like all the other trees of its botanical genus. But that need not blind us to the fact that it was called *fir* by every Scots-speaking Scot for hundreds of years before his day. Many of the trees that Scott planted may still be seen in the Abbotsford policies; some of the outlying woods have, in recent years, been replanted by the Forestry Commission.

Opposite Abbotsford, the Gala Water flows in from the north; the busy textile town of Galashiels is overlooked by wooded Gala Hill, 904 feet high, which lost all

The Forest of Elibank and Traquair, deep in the dale of the Tweed, between Peebles and Galashiels.

its trees during the last war, but has since been replanted. The long dale of Gala Water, traversed by the high road and railway to Edinburgh, lies in Midlothian, not usually considered a Border County. Around Stow and Fountainhall it has all the character of a Highland glen, with a narrow band of tilled fields on its level floor, a fringe of woodland on the dale sides, and broad expanses of treeless pastures running up the fells beyond. Much of the daleside wood is broadleaved, with wych elm as the leading tree; it thrives on slopes too steep for either ploughman or grazier. Higher up the dale, around Heriot, stand a cluster of coniferous shelter belts and blocks, planted to protect sheep from winter blizzards.

Back in the main dale of the Tweed, we find on its south bank, between Selkirk and Caddonfoot, the national forest of Yair Hill, which extends to 2,300 acres. The land rises from the river up the steep slopes to the Three Brethren Cairns, crowning a hill 1,523 feet high which forms a local landmark visited each year by the Common Riders from Selkirk. Afforestation began here in 1950, and has been carried out largely with spruces. Most of the ground is ploughed prior to planting. This forest is named after the mansion house of Yair in the Tweed vale below.

A few miles farther upstream, the old estates of Elibank in Selkirkshire and Traquair in Peebles-shire give their names to the Elibank and Traquair Forest, of 6,400 acres. Elibank possesses a ruined keep, while Traquair House is a grand example of Scots baronial architecture. This forest runs high up the steep southern flanks of the dale to the Minch Muir, 1,856 feet above sea level. Afforestation began here in 1945, and most of the ground is ploughed prior to planting. The main trees are spruces, larches, and pines. The young plantations are now clearly apparent from the main road that runs through the weaving towns of Walkerburn and Innerleithen, on the north bank of the Tweed. They are approached by the secondary road along the south bank.

The Plora Burn, close to Elibank Forest, is the scene of the famous poem *Bonny Kilmeny*, written by James Hogg, the Ettrick Shepherd, who once dwelt nearby. Evoking in a few brief lines the haunting beauty of the quiet pastoral dale of the Tweed, it tells how:

"Bonny Kilmeny gaed up the glen
. . . . to hear the yorlin sing,
And pu' the cress-flower round the spring;
The scarlet hypp and the hindberrye,
And the nut that hung frae the hazel tree."

The yorlin is that bright little bunting the yellowhammer, while the hindberrye is the luscious wild raspberry, common in the shaws beside the upland burns.

Somewhere up in these hills must surely still grow the famous "Bush aboon Traquair", a trysting place for lovers that inspired lyric poets.

Higher up the dale the young forest of Cardrona, also on the south bank, comes plainly into view; its fire tower, standing on a high bluff, is a well-known landmark for travellers. The planting of Cardrona Forest, which extends to 1,800 acres, began in 1935, and was carried out with pines, larches, spruces, and a good deal of Douglas fir. Growth has been rapid, and thinnings are in full swing. Several timber houses have been built for the forestry workers. This forest is named after Cardrona Castle, an ancient Border keep, and the Cardrona estate which has a modern mansion.

Glentress and Peebles Town

In 1919, shortly after its foundation, the Forestry Commission combined with the Department of Agriculture for Scotland in a joint scheme of afforestation and land settlement at Glentress, just east of Peebles. Here an estate of 1,000 acres was taken over, and the better ground divided into small-holdings, which have continued to prosper; the poorer and steeper ground was afforested. Subsequently there have been extensions over blocks of cleared woodland on the Ven Law north of Peebles, and on Cademuir Hill to the south-west. Glentress Forest now embraces 2,400 acres. The main portion consists of two fine glens, Shielgreen close to the Peebles Hydro and Eshiels farther east; both names contain the "shieling" element which shows that they once held the summer grazings of Norse settlements farther down the dale. At its highest point, Dunslair Heights, 1,975 feet above sea level, Glentress commands a fine panoramic view of the lonely Moorfoot Hills stretching far to the north.

A wide variety of coniferous trees has been planted at Glentress, including Scots pine, European and Japanese larches, Norway and Sitka spruces, Douglas fir, and the grand silver fir, *Abies grandis;* there are also small areas of hardwood trees such as beech and sycamore. Several stands include "sample plots", which are measured at intervals of a few years to discover how fast the trees are growing and producing timber. A network of forest roads wind up the glens, and down these come poles and timber harvested in thinnings. Forestry has proved a productive use for these poor, steep hillsides, and it provides steady work for local men. In the higher reaches of Glentress Forest, a trial is being made of the maintenance of perpetual tree cover, avoiding clear fellings.

Just above the grey-stone town of Peebles, with its busy textile mills, the road up the Tweed winds below Neidpath Castle, a keep preserved intact ever since the troublous times of English invaders. Behind the castle, a fine wood of beech and sycamore now rises up a steep slope, but things looked otherwise when the poet William Wordsworth passed down the valley in 1803. At that date the fourth Marquess of Queensberry had just felled this wood, and Wordsworth launched an indignant sonnet against him, describing him as "Degenerate Douglas" who had "levelled with the dust a noble horde, a brotherhood of venerable trees".

North of Peebles runs the narrow dale of the Eddleston Water, followed by the road towards Edinburgh. It holds a considerable extent of woodland, grouped around Darn Hall and Portmore House, well up the dale. Further north, around Leadburn, shelter belts and blocks protect the high upland grazings where the open moors are crossed. The Commission's Eddleston Water Forest, of 1,400 acres, is made up of many scattered sprucewoods on these wild uplands.

The Upper Dale of the Tweed

Above Peebles the valley of the Tweed loses its gorge-like character and broadens out into a pastoral vale, everywhere over 600 feet above sea level and surrounded by green rolling hills approaching 2,000 feet in elevation. Sheep grazing is the ruling occupation, but several large woods lie along the main dale. Towards the north, the Lyne Water, coming down from the far Pentlands, flows through an elevated yet sheltered plateau, around West Linton. Here mixed farming is maintained as high as 800 feet up, with the aid of shelterbelts of conifers and beeches. Close to the village of Stobo in the main dale the Commission has its Dreva Forest, where 1,400 acres of cleared woodland has been planted up.

The Dawyck estate, situated close to Stobo and some six miles west of Peebles, has the largest wooded area on the upper Tweed. There are nearly 1,000 acres of woodlands, and they run far up the slopes of Pykestone Hill and Scawd Law to an elevation of 1,500 feet. Dawyck has a notable history of tree planting. From 1450 to

1691 it was owned by the Veitch family, who planted the introduced horse chestnut in their policies as early as 1650. From 1691 it was owned by the Naesmyths, who planted here, in 1725, one of the oldest larches in Scotland; they added several new silver firs between 1831 and 1850, and the Douglas fir as early as 1835. In 1897 Dawyck was purchased by its present owners, the Balfours, who have devoted much attention to both ornamental trees and timber crops. The world-famous and very beautiful arboretum here is the first home of the Dawyck beech, an ornamental variety in which all the side branches trend upwards, as in a Lombardy poplar. It was first discovered growing wild in an estate beechwood, and has since been propagated by grafting. Another rarity is a specimen of Brewer's weeping spruce, *Picea breweriana*, lifted from the wilds of Oregon by Col. F. R. S. Balfour in 1908.

The Balfours established many trial plots of the newer and less usual forest trees, and so provided a valuable guide to the Forestry Commission and private foresters concerning their prospects in Scottish plantations. For example, a plot of the rare but attractive Oriental spruce, *Picea orientalis*, from the Caucasus, has been shown to thrive here and to produce timber at a rate comparable to the common Norway spruce. The western white pine, *Pinus monticola*, from California, grows as fast as the Corsican pine, though unfortunately it suffers from rust fungus. Dawyck is a stern proving ground, for this valley is notoriously cold and frosty in winter, and is swept by fierce winds; temperatures as low as zero Fahrenheit are often recorded. Other spruces represented in the trial plots are *Picea rubra* and *P. engelmanni* from North America, *P. omorika* from Serbia, and *P. asperata* from China. There are also trials of two North American

PLATE 38
Ploughing the Border moors in readiness for tree planting. The giant tractor-drawn plough cuts drainage furrows and throws up ribbons of turf to receive young spruces.

PLATE 39
Thinning in progress at a twenty-year-old Border spruce forest. The smaller, less shapely trees are removed first, and are dragged to a rackway to await transport to a chipboard mill.

silver firs, *Abies grandis* and *A. lowiana*. A noteworthy plantation of the American balsam poplar, *Populus trichocarpa*, shows the possibilities of this quick-growing broad-leaved tree in our upland regions.

The largest tree in the Dawyck arboretum is a Douglas fir planted in 1835. It is 131 feet high, 133 years old, 17 feet round, and has a timber volume of 700 hoppus feet. There is a rich collection of spruces, while the scarce silver firs include *Abies squamata*, *A. georgii*, *A. koreana*, and *A. mariesii*.

On the Rachan estate nearby there are 400 acres of plantations, largely of conifers, but including some beech and ash thriving at heights over 600 feet above sea level. The Tomb Wood here is one of the finest stands of Scots pine in the country; it carries 160 trees to the acre, 80 feet in height, and 4 feet in girth, showing a volume of 9,000 hoppus feet to the acre. Several individual pines

are classed as "elite", and have been selected as parents for tree breeding.

Close to Rachan the dale of the Tweed trends suddenly southward, to run far up into the grassy hills, for twenty miles past Tweedsmuir to the river's source at Tweed's Well, not far from Moffat. This dale, once bare of woods, is now the scene of one of the Commission's major enterprises in the Borders—Glenbreck Forest of 9,500 acres, which stands beside the road to the Devil's Beef Tub viewpoint.

Selkirkshire

In days gone by the modern county of Selkirk was known as Ettrick Forest, a hunting ground of the Scottish kings which was famous for its tall oaks and wild deer. The old ballad aptly describes it:

"Ettrick Forest is a fair forest
  In it grows many a semelie trie
  The hart, the hynd, the dae, the rae
  And of a' beasts great plentie"

But today Selkirk is one of the least wooded counties of Scotland, with only 3 per cent of its land under trees. The small area of woodland, some 5,000 acres, is nearly all concentrated down towards the Tweed, within a few miles of Selkirk town. The upper dales of the Ettrick and Yarrow Waters are almost devoid of woods, and indeed even of trees.

In the dale of the Yarrow, on the braes above the north side of St. Mary's Loch, an odd cluster of hazel clings precariously to a patch of scree where the sheep seldom graze. The Ettrick dale can claim a few planta-tions near Thirlestane House, and one at Tushielaw. But otherwise all the trees of these rolling hills have vanished before the onslaught of the sheep. Once peaceful times had come to the Borders, it proved profitable for the farmers to concentrate on great sheep runs, and grazing continues to be the main use of the land today. Gradually the forest disappeared, for all the young seedling trees got bitten back. Significantly, there is little birch scrub in Selkirkshire; any woodland that is cleared is promptly invaded by sheep and no birch seedlings survive.

Close to Selkirk town there are two private estates, Bowhill and Philliphaugh, that are noted for their skilled and intensive management. Bowhill, owned by the Duke of Buccleuch, occupies 1,400 acres in the dales

PLATE 40
Measuring the thinnings. A sample of logs from every batch is measured for length and girth, so that its timber volume and value can be cal-culated.

75

of the Yarrow and the Ettrick Waters, west of Selkirk town; it is comprised of three main blocks, named Blackandrew, Old Wark Burn, and Bowhill; the land rises from 420 feet at the meeting of the waters to 1,200 feet at Blackandrew, and the region enjoys a pleasant climate with a rainfall of only thirty inches a year. A wide variety of trees, both coniferous and broadleaved, are grown, sometimes as pure crops but often in intimate mixture. Natural regeneration is frequently employed for re-stocking the woods, for many kinds of tree are found to come up freely from seed. There is an estate sawmill and also a forest nursery. The trees grown at Bowhill include Scots pine, Norway and Sitka spruces, European and hybrid larches, Douglas fir, Lawson cypress, western hemlock, sycamore, oak, ash, beech, and birch. An expanse of 150 acres of birch scrub at Howebottom is believed to have survived, without more recent planting, from the ancient Forest of Ettrick.

The Philliphaugh estate, just across the river from Selkirk town, is owned by Sir Samuel Strang Steel, a Forestry Commissioner. His woods include vigorous plantations of most of the common conifers, while hardwoods such as ash and sycamore also flourish and produce crops of natural seedlings.

Roxburghshire

Climbing steeply out of Selkirk, we follow the winding road across the hills towards Hawick. Away to the north-east the basin of the Teviot opens out, its fertile fields shielded by an elaborate pattern of shelterbelts, most of them running at right angles to the strong south-westerly winds; some climb to 800 feet above sea level. Here and there the belts broaden out into larger timber-growing plantations, particularly in the neighbourhood of the great mansion houses. By contrast, the land to the south-west forms one great sea of grassy sheep pastures, stretching clear away to Hart Fell and Ettrick Pen in distant Dumfries-shire.

From Hawick, that prosperous textile town isolated amid these lovely but lonely hills, we turn west up the Borthwick Water. Close to the village of Roberton lie two private estates which maintain thriving woodlands well up amid the hills, at elevations of 700 to 1,000 feet. In the Borthwickbrae Plantation, south of the road, there are 170 acres of woods and shelterbelts, which include spruces and Japanese larch growing in very exposed situations. Borthwickshields estate, away to the north of the road, has 120 acres of woods, which include oak, ash, and beech, as well as Serbian spruce and the commoner conifers.

Up on the remote headwaters of the Borthwick Water, the Commission has been planting, since 1948, the young spruce forest called Craik, covering 8,000 acres. Most of the ground lies above 800 feet in elevation, running up to 1,400 feet on Ewelair Hill; all round lie the trackless hills, and there is no road, nor indeed any track better than a shepherd's path, over into the surrounding dales. A group of houses has been built for the forest workers who tend the trees of these isolated woods.

Away down the Teviot from Hawick, close to the village of Denholm, the woodlands of the Wells estate occupy 300 acres in the dale of the Rule Water; they rise to a height of 1,200 feet on the slopes of Rubers Law, a well-known Border landmark. Beech, oak, sycamore, and lime thrive well on the lower and more fertile ground, while pines, spruces, and larches are grown higher up the braes.

Jedburgh, in the next valley, that of the Jed Water, is famous for its ruined abbey, founded by David I in 1118. All the hinterland to the south was known as Jed Forest, and the monks of Jedburgh held extensive rights to pasture their sheep and cattle there. Gradually the woods disappeared as the seedlings were browsed back, but the fringes of the native elm, ash, oak, birch, rowan, and alder survive along the steep banks of the winding river. When you follow the high road south towards Carter Bar, the landscape opens out into a wide expanse of hill pastures, reaching north as far as Kelso, and west as far as Hawick, while the long spine of the high Cheviots forms an encircling frame on the south and east. A feature of these uplands, where sheep and cattle graze in winter at levels around 1,000 feet, is the presence of small square shelter blocks of Scots pine and spruce. When the blizzards descend, the beasts draw down into the lee sides of these blocks, and enjoy the protection given against freezing winds and drifting snow.

Away in a hollow of the Cheviots lies one of the remotest woods in Scotland, though oddly enough it lies right against the English Border. Known as Leithope, it stands above the lonely farmstead of Hindhope at the head of the Kale Water. Here 1,200 acres of hill ground was planted up, between 1947 and 1957, with Norway and Sitka spruces, to form part of the Commission's Wauchope Forest. Only a lonely hill road, thirteen miles long, links Leithope with Jedburgh, though it is barely a couple of miles from the busy Carter Bar road, on the English side of the Border in Redesdale.

Border Forest Park—*Plates 2, 3 and 38 to 41*

We next take the high road from Hawick towards Carter Bar as far as Bonchester Bridge. There, down in the valley of the Rule Water, lies a group of houses built for the workers in Wauchope Forest, where planting began in 1939. A vast forest this, covering 17,000 acres of the fells; out of this some 5,000 acres are set aside as hill grazings. The spruces—Norway and Sitka, together with a little Lodgepole pine, are virtually the only trees grown at Wauchope, for the combination of peaty soil, exposure, and high rainfall suit them but no other trees.

All the ground is ploughed prior to planting, by great hill drainage ploughs, drawn by powerful tractors, which turn out long slices of turf wherein the young trees are planted.

Wauchope Forest forms part of the great Border Forest Park, which includes Newcastleton Forest in Liddesdale, as well as the English forests of Redesdale and Kielder in Northumberland. The main attraction to the visitor to Wauchope is the grand range of hills that border it to the south, with summits lying above the limit of timber growing. In turn these hills are: Windburgh Hill, 1,662 feet, Fanna Hill, Needs Law, all on the march with Liddesdale; Hartshorn Pike, the rocks called the Carlin's (or Old Wife's) Tooth, Knox Knowe, and Carter Fell (1,815 feet) along the actual English Border, forming the march with Northumberland. All fair walking country this, for the man who does not mind a long tramp over rock and peat through country that is rich in legend and romance.

The high road east from Bonchester Bridge passes the ruined Southdean (or Souden) Kirk, where The Douglas mustered his men for the raid that ended in mortal conflict with The Percy at the Battle of Otterburn in 1388—a tale still told in the ballads called *Chevy Chase* and *Otterburn*. Carter Bar, a little to the east of Wauchope, forms a fine elevated crossing over into Redesdale—used by travellers along the modern road to Newcastle, just as it was by the Border reivers centuries ago. The Carterhaugh country around it is the scene of that fascinating ballad of the supernatural, concerning the

PLATE 41
Loading spruce logs in a Border forest.

fair Janet and her elfin lover, known as *Tam Lin*. Knox Knowe and the Kielder Stone have heard the ring of steel, and the hoof-beats of armed raiders from either side, on perilous excursions over the Border Hills.

Liddesdale and Newcastleton

Great new forests of spruce are supplanting the sheep runs on many of the Eskdale and Liddesdale hillsides, where the fertility built up by ancient, vanished woods had become exhausted. One of the oldest Forestry Commission enterprises is the Forest of Newcastleton, which covers 7,700 acres, mainly on the eastern side of the Liddel valley in Roxburghshire. It marches with the great Kielder Forest over in Northumberland, and with Kershope Forest in Cumberland, to form a part of the Border Forest Park, which embraces in all no less than 125,000 acres.

Here, on the braes a mile or so to the east of Newcastleton town, the Commission's foresters began, in 1921, to lay out the trim rows of Norway and Sitka spruce trees. Growth was slow at first, but gradually new techniques were discovered. After some years, the new trees were planted in turfs cut from the drains, instead of being set directly in the soil. Later great tractor-drawn ploughs were used to speed the work of drainage, combined with turf formation. Meanwhile those trees that had been planted earlier grew steadily upwards, to form a smooth green canopy topped by slender conical spires. At length roads were run along the grassy rides that had been left unplanted, to serve as firebreaks, and the thinning out of the woods, now thirty feet tall, began.

Since 1948, a steady stream of sound poles has been harvested each year from these woods, which even now are barely fifty years old. At first the poles were so small that they could serve only as fence stakes or rails; then pitprops were cut from them. Some material may nowadays go to a modern factory at Annan on the Solway, to be fabricated into chipboard, the wonderful man-made timber that has countless uses in building and furniture manufacture. Other poles may go to Workington in Cumberland to become food cartons and some as far as Ellesmere Port in Cheshire to become newsprint. This small forest employs around forty men, steadily throughout the year; most of them come from Newcastleton, where a group of new houses has been built for forestry workers. Here, as elsewhere in Scotland, we find that the advent of modern afforestation has brought with it work for more hands than the land could previously support; the drift from the rural districts has been halted, and men have come back from the towns to play their part in creating and harvesting this new resource.

The choice of spruces as the main trees to plant at Newcastleton rested largely on the pioneer work of the Duke of Buccleuch, who had established, about the year 1913, a pioneer plantation on his lands of Muirburnhead, some four miles south-west of Newcastleton and on the western side of Liddesdale, in Dumfriesshire. This big wood, covering some 500 acres, had shown remarkable promise, and it was clear that the spruces were well suited to the peaty soils and ample rainfall of the Borders. These soils have been formed above a thick layer of Boulder Clay, left by the Ice Age glaciers on top of the underlying Carboniferous or coal-bearing rocks. In days gone by some of the farmers dug out coal from small outcrops, as a change from their usual peat fuel, but the shallow coal seams have never been worked commercially.

Profitable Spruce Trees

Everyone knows the Norway spruce as the common Christmas tree, and it has been grown in Scotland, by enterprising land-owners, for nearly three centuries. The Sitka spruce is a comparative newcomer and much less familiar; it comes from British Columbia and Alaska, and its great merits are extreme hardihood and rapid growth. You can tell it from the Norway spruce because its leaves or needles are bluish green and sharply pointed. The woods of both spruces are much alike; that of the Norway spruce is imported in vast quantities, as "whitewood", from Scandinavia and the Baltic, especially for joinery and box making. The chief merits of the spruce timbers are their clean white appearance and ready working qualities, combined with sufficient strength for most everyday uses. They yield good veneers for plywood, good chips for chipboard, good fibres for fibreboards, and excellent pulp for making paper, cellophane, or artificial silks and rayons. Even their sawdust has its uses—as wood flour for a filler in plastics. Today when so much wood is used in some reconstituted or manufactured form, the spruces are often preferred to much stronger or more durable timbers like beech and oak. Their sapwood can even be made durable by modern preservatives. These useful virtues of suitability to local conditions, and adaptability to manifold uses, account for the widespread use of the spruces on the Border hills, not only by the Forestry Commission but by private owners too. As a shelterbelt tree, Sitka spruce has here no equal.

Eskdale

Travelling down Liddesdale to Canonbie in Dumfriesshire, we reach the valley of the Border Esk, and from there up towards Langholm woodlands of another character line the slopes of Eskdale. These are the relics of the old native broadleaved woods of oak and wych elm, birch and alder, which have been enriched by planting Scots pine, larches, spruces, and occasional beeches and sycamores. Hence they present a pleasing variety of trees, and as a succession of ages is represented, we find associated the charms of youthful saplings and the grandeur of stately veterans. It is possible, by skilled management, to preserve this attractive mixture indefinitely. The forester does not always need to clear fell his crop at one clean sweep. Where conditions are right, he can select suitable mature trees that are ripe for harvesting, and thin out the groups of the younger ones that are jostling one another too closely. Nature will provide ample seedlings or saplings to fill in the gaps, but only where the natural foes of such young trees—sheep, deer and rabbits, are either absent or else kept under very close control.

This method of management is known as a "selection system", while the process of ensuring the regrowth of the old stand, without replanting, is called "natural regeneration". Work of this kind is carried out in the Duke of Buccleuch's Langholm woods, and ensures a steady harvest of timber without ever stripping bare the sylvan fringes of this picturesque valley. The Duke owns around 4,000 acres of woodland between the Rivers Esk and Liddel, and about one-quarter of this carries broadleaved trees.

Above Langholm the main road north to Hawick follows the dale of the Ewes Water, and on each side of this many of the scattered farms have shelterbelts or blocks of conifers. In summer the passer-by may wonder what purpose these small and windswept plantations may serve, but in winter their purpose is obvious enough. When blizzards sweep the hills, the sheep draw down to the woods, and shelter either in their lee or below their trees; these *bields*, in a bad winter, can make all the difference between survival and disaster.

A secondary road follows the course of the main River Esk north-west from Langholm to wind over fifty miles of the lonely hills towards Yarrow and Peebles. Eight miles above Langholm, where the two tributary streams of Black Esk and White Esk unite, stands the big new forest called Castle O'er, which has an area of 9,400 acres. Here the peaty soils, which overlie Silurian rocks, had proved too poor for profitable sheep grazing to be maintained. Since 1938 the Forestry Commission has been afforesting them with spruces, and recently private concerns have lent a hand, so new houses have had to be built in this lonely hill country. Most of the land has been ploughed before planting, and this modern technique has resulted in rapid and vigorous growth right from the outset.

Annandale—*Plates 1 and 44*

Annandale is known to thousands of travellers as the route of the main road and railway south from Glasgow and the central Lowlands to Carlisle and England. Its upper reaches, where road and rail cross over from the upper dale of the Clyde at an altitude of 1,000 feet, are wild and windswept, and in severe winters the blizzards sometimes halt the road traffic. But as one proceeds south down its fifty-mile stretch, conditions become steadily kinder and milder, and its southern reaches, where it winds through the low hills facing south to the Solway, between Lockerbie and Annan, provide one of the most fertile and smiling landscapes in Scotland.

The highest forest on the Elvan Water, above Annandale, is the Commission's property called Greskine, which lies on the western side near the summit of the pass. As seen from the high road, which here follows the eastern flank, it presents a broad panorama of green sprucewoods, which are gradually being extended to cover 11,000 acres of the hillsides. The railway line gives a closer view, for the plantations come right down to the famous Beattock Bank, except for a strip of green pasture land which is carefully preserved to serve as a firebreak. Northward-bound trains climb so slowly that travellers have ample time to observe the new forest roads, and the piles of pit props and other produce that are being brought out as thinnings from this young forest. The northern reaches of this forest run up to an elevation of 1,600 feet on Mount Hill. There are also woods around Auchencastle House, where the soils are more fertile and the ground more sheltered, and some oak, beech, and poplar trees are grown. Planting at Greskine began in 1917.

Two other Commission areas in the Annandale region follow the typical pattern of spruce planting on high and exposed grassy hillsides. Moffat Water Forest covers 6,000 acres of Moffat Dale, along the picturesque road to St. Mary's Loch, Yarrow and Selkirk. The Auchenroddan block of Castle O'er Forest, covering 800 acres, lies on the eastern side of Annandale itself, roughly midway between Moffat and Lockerbie. This preference for spruce is also manifested on a number of private estates, for on these peaty soils, where thick deposits of Boulder Clay overly the old Silurian rocks, and under the prevailing high rainfall and severe exposure, no other tree thrives so readily.

Rather different Commission woodlands are found at the St. Ann's portion of Greskine Forest, a property of 1,000 acres bordering the high road from Moffat to Dumfries. Here most of the land had previously been under tree crops, as part of a large private estate, and it held a richer store of fertility. The ground lies lower too, and hence enjoys more sun and suffers less rain. So the foresters were able to vary their tree crops, and to plant some of the more exacting conifers like larch and Douglas fir, and hardwoods such as oak and beech. Also in this favoured zone lies Brownmoor Forest, made up of a number of scattered blocks, having a total area of 900 acres, around Lockerbie and Ecclefechan. Most of these areas have long been under trees, being hillsides too steep for agriculture, though lying on the very fertile Calciferous Sandstone rocks. Climate and soil are so favourable that some planting has been done with broadleaved trees, including oak, beech, ash, sycamore, and wych elm.

One of the leading private estates in this pleasant district is that called Castle Milk, beside the quaintly-named stream the Water of Milk, just south of Lockerbie. It has its own sawmill and a big expanse of conifer woods, which show remarkably rapid rates of growth, while its policies hold fine avenues of hardwoods, particularly beech, and many tall specimen trees.

Chipboard at Annan

The small town and seaport of Annan, where the River Annan flows out into the Solway, has been since 1955 the home of a modern factory that makes chipboards from the trees removed in thinnings in forests and plantations on either side of the Border. It was chosen because, within a distance of sixty miles, which is a workable journey for a lorry, there was assurance of ample supplies of suitable timber to keep its continuous process going indefinitely. The firm concerned, Messrs. Airscrew Weyroc, already had much experience of making chipboard, or reconstituted wood, from factory wastes in the London region; and it saw that by getting raw material fresh from the Border forests, it would be able to obtain a more uniform and higher quality product.

The process, in brief, is to break down round logs into small chips, and then to mix them with a plastic resin that binds them together; this mixture is spread out in a flat layer, and then treated with heat and pressure so that the resin grips the chips and produces a broad flat sheet of re-made wood. In practice, all this is carried out without a pause, the chips pouring into the train of machines to emerge as a long slab of chipboard that is then sawn across to provide handy pieces. Chipboard is widely used in the building and furniture trades, largely because of its even texture, its availability in handier sizes than planks of timber, and its freedom from pronounced shrinkage. It is not so much a substitute for wood, as another form of wood that proves better for some jobs than its parent material. Its value is such that it can bear transport charges to any part of the British Isles, and indeed to consuming centres overseas.

From the forester's point of view the chipboard, food carton and paper trades provide a useful outlet for his smaller trees. Because all the wood can be used, there is little of the waste in the cutting away of slabs, or irregular side pieces, that occurs in a sawmill; only the bark need be stripped away. Further, the chipping machines can take a fair range of sizes of small logs, cut to standard lengths but having various diameters. It is not necessary to cut them to the strict dimensions needed for other jobs, such as pit props; while the calculation of their volume for sale is also easier. Quite a number of coniferous trees can be used, but the spruces are preferred, with pines second; these are the leading trees in the Border forests, and their marketing at a remunerative price has been made much easier.

Forest of Ae—*Plates 42 and 43*

The Water of Ae is a short tumultuous river, subject to sudden spates, which rises on the magnificent hill called Queensberry, 2,285 feet high, and runs into the Annan near Lochmaben. The origin of its name, pronounced like the letter A, is the old Norse word *aa*, meaning a brook or rivulet. This name is now shared with the modern Forest of Ae and with Ae Village, the first village to be built in Scotland solely for a community of foresters. The general aspect of its countryside is much like that around Newcastleton; for although the rocks here are Silurian and not Carboniferous, they are buried deeply below a similar mantle of Boulder Clay, topped by a layer of peat. It was this peat, in fact, that by its steady accumulation caused the decline of good sheep pastures, to the point where afforestation became a more productive and profitable use for the hill slopes. In 1927 the Commission made its first acquisition of land near the present Ae Village, which lies eleven miles north-east from Dumfries, and some two miles north-west of the main road to Moffat. The planting of Norway and Sitka spruces, on the same lines as those developed at Newcastleton, has gone on steadily ever since, while some of the less peaty slopes have been planted with Scots pine and Japanese larch. Successive additions have raised the extent of the forest to 13,500 acres.

When afforestation began there were only half-a-dozen shepherds' cottages scattered over all this vast expanse, but the need for labour soon led to a group of smallholdings, and also a small school, being established in the valley of the Windyhill Burn. By 1945, the oldest plantations were ready for thinning, a task that has gone on ever since to supply fence material for local farms, pit props for the Dumfriesshire and Ayrshire coal-fields, raw material for chipboard and packaging board factories and paper pulp mills, and logs for local sawmills. Soon over seventy people were finding work in the woods, more than could hope to find housing in this region of scattered homesteads. It was decided, therefore, to build a new forest village, and in 1947 this work was inaugurated by the Rt. Hon. Thomas Johnston, a former Secretary of State for Scotland. The site has been carefully chosen, on a hillock, safely above the flood level of the Water of Ae. Thirty houses, a village hall, a shop, and a forest depot have been set up, while a new school has been opened for the foresters' youngsters, and playing fields have been provided. The road past the new village, with its attractive white-walled dwellings, winds up the Windyhill Burn to Loch

PLATE 42
Hauling out thinnings from the vast sprucewoods of the Forest of Ae north of Dumfries.

Ettrick, and thence down to Closeburn, affording wonderful views over the thriving green spruce woods and up the main valley of the Water of Ae. A network of forest roads, with bridges over the streams, has been constructed to open up this outlying hill country. Farther west, where the Cairn Water wanders down from the sleepy little township of Moniaive, embowered amid the green hills, is the young forest of Dalmacallan; this covers 3,200 acres, and planting was begun in 1948.

The town of Dumfries is the centre of Forestry Commission activities in the South of Scotland generally. Close beside it lie the peat wastes of the level Lochar Moss, which runs out towards the Solway; several plantations of pines and spruces have been made on its surface, some by private landowners and some by the Commission. Its deep, heathery peat gives the forester major problems of drainage and tree nutrition, but

these are being overcome by the use of draining machines and the application of phosphate fertilisers.

Nithsdale and Drumlanrig

Travelling north from Dumfries, by road or rail, up the dale of the winding River Nith, the traveller passes for several miles through the well-tended estates of the Duke of Buccleuch and Queensberry, whose principal seat is Drumlanrig Castle, close to Thornhill. Here the fertile ploughlands of the dale blend with the widespread woods and the hill pastures to provide a landscape showing an ideal marriage of farming and forestry. The woods occupy ground too steep, rocky, or poor to merit attention from the farmer, yet at the same time they shelter his better land. The Duke, who is one of the leading landowners concerned with forestry in Scotland, has here some 9,200 acres under trees, and these

PLATE 43
Forest workers houses in the heart of the Forest of Ae.

woodlands provide employment for nearly one hundred men on planting, tending and timber harvesting.

The situation of these woods in a southward-running dale is a particularly favoured one, for the hills to west, north, and east shelter them from the worst of winter's weather; while many stand on sandstones more fertile than the surrounding Silurian rocks. Therefore it proves possible to grow broadleaved trees of good size and quality, including oak, ash, beech, and sycamore. There are 2,000 acres of enclosed broadleaved woodlands, with a further 1,200 acres of open oak and birch higher up the braes. Coniferous plantations on the less fertile ground occupy 6,000 acres, and on the dale-sides several sorts thrive, particularly Norway and Sitka spruces, Japanese and hybrid larches, Scots pine, and Douglas fir. In the most exposed and peaty places, the hardy Sitka spruce, as elsewhere in the Borders, proves the leading tree.

Besides the Buccleuch properties, there are several smaller private estates in Nithsdale, and on these also a high standard of woodland management is maintained. But as one goes north to the head of the dale, around the coal mines of Sanquhar, the uplands become wild, bleak, and treeless. Nevertheless there was a great Forest of Sanquhar in the thirteenth century, and today the plantations of the Eliock estate prove that spruces, Japanese larch, and even Douglas fir can be profitably grown amid those inhospitable surroundings. On the westerly side of the dale, the Commission has started a new forest called Upper Nithsdale, covering 3,200 acres.

Dumfries-shire can claim the tallest recorded Norway spruce in Scotland, a tree 144 feet in height which grows at Sprinkell. It also holds Scotland's tallest lime, which stands at Barjarg and is 127 feet high.

PLATE 44
Greskine Forest above Moffat in Dumfries-shire, close to the main road (A.74) and railway from Glasgow to Carlisle.

Shelterbelts on Tinto Hill, near Symington, Upper Clydesdale.

NOTES

Metric Units: Conversions

1 foot = 0·305 metres.   1 metre = 3·281 feet.   1 acre = 0·405 hectares.   1 hectare = 2·471 acres.
1 hoppus foot (timber measure) = 0·036 cubic metres.   1 cubic metre = 27·7 hoppus feet.

PLATE 46

Ledmore Nursery, north of Perth. A forester examines transplanted pines; a transplanting team is at work on the far slope.

COMMISSION FORESTS
IN SCOTLAND

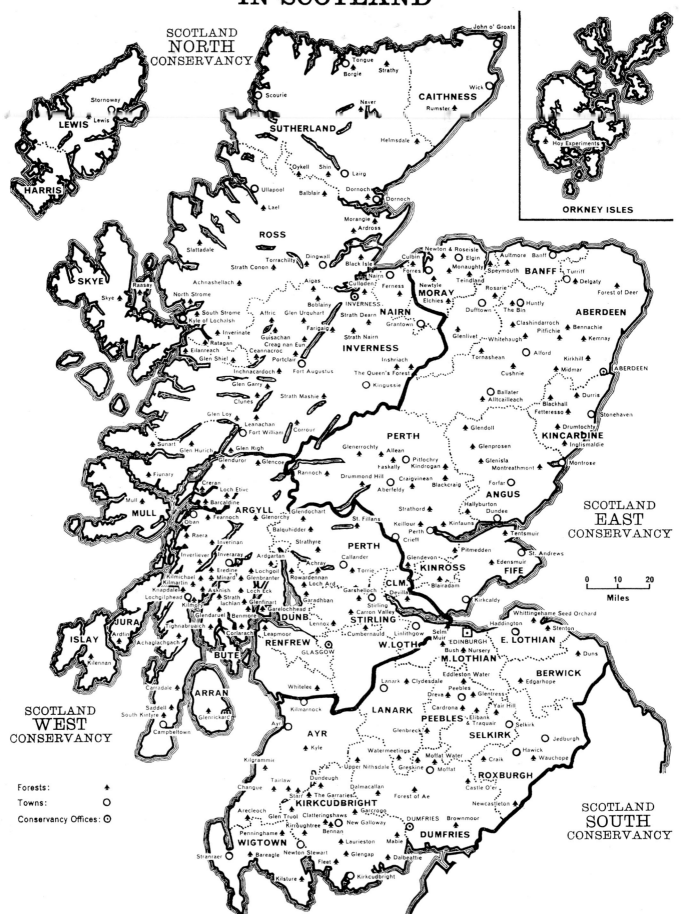

SCOTLAND
NORTH
CONSERVANCY

SCOTLAND
EAST
CONSERVANCY

SCOTLAND
WEST
CONSERVANCY

SCOTLAND
SOUTH
CONSERVANCY

ORKNEY ISLES

Forests: ▲
Towns: ◯
Conservancy Offices: ⊙

0   10   20
Miles

THE FORESTRY COMMISSION

Senior Officer for Scotland: 25 Drumsheugh Gardens, Edinburgh 3 (031–225 4782)

Research: Government Buildings, Bankhead Avenue, Sighthill, Edinburgh 11 (031–443 4010), and at the Edinburgh Centre of Rural Economy, Bush Estate, three miles north-west of Penicuik, Midlothian.

North Conservancy

Forestry Commission,
60 Church Street,
Inverness
(OIN–3 32811)

Caithness, Sutherland, Ross and Cromarty, Inverness, part Argyll (Mull and areas west of Loch Linnhe), Nairn (except north-east corner), Moray (southern areas only), Orkney, Shetland.

East Conservancy

Forestry Commission,
6 Queen's Gate,
Aberdeen
(OAB–4 33361)

Nairn (north-east corner only), Moray (except southern areas), Banff, Aberdeen, Kincardine, Angus, Kinross, Fife (except south-west corner), part Perth (areas north and east of Crieff).

South Conservancy

Forestry Commission,
Greystone Park,
Moffat Road,
Dumfries
(ODU–7 2425)

Midlothian, East Lothian, Berwick, Roxburgh, Selkirk, Peebles, Dumfries, Kirkcudbright, Wigtown, part Ayr (south of Kilmarnock), part Lanarkshire (south-east of Lanark).

West Conservancy

Forestry Commission,
20 Renfrew Street,
Glasgow, C.2
(041–DOU 7261)

Argyll (except Mull and areas west of Loch Linnhe), part Perth (areas west of Crieff), Stirling, Dunbarton, Renfrew, Clackmannan, part Fife (south-west corner only), part Ayr (north of Kilmarnock), part Lanarkshire (north-west of Lanark), West Lothian, Bute.

Other useful addresses:

Royal Scottish Forestry Society, 25 Drumsheugh Gardens, Edinburgh 3 (*Caledonian* 7402).
Scottish Woodland Owners' Association Ltd., 6 Chester Street, Edinburgh 3 (*Caledonian* 1905).

✿　　✿　　✿　　✿　　✿

Illustrated Guide Books to the Forest Parks and other wooded areas in Scotland are published by Her Majesty's Stationery Office at the prices set out below. These and other priced publications are obtainable from Her Majesty's Stationery Office, 13a Castle Street, Edinburgh 2, or through any bookseller.

Argyll Forest Park	7s. (post 8d.)
Border Forest Park	5s. (post 8d.)
Glen More Forest Park (Cairngorms)	8s. 6d. (post 8d.)
Glen Trool Forest Park (Galloway)	6s. (post 8d.)
Queen Elizabeth Forest Park (Trossachs)	3s. 6d. (post 8d.)
Short Guide to Queen Elizabeth Forest Park	1s. (post 4d.)
Forests of North-East Scotland	5s. (post 8d.)

Booklet No. 6, Forest Parks, outlines each Park, the Arboreta and the New Forest .. .. 2s. 6d. (post 6d.)

Booklet No. 15, Know your Conifers, gives a short illustrated account of the most important British conifers .. .. 5s. (post 10d.)

A full list of Forestry Commission publications and two leaflets, *Camping in the Forest Parks* and *Forestry in Scotland* are available, free, from the Forestry Commission, 25 Drumsheugh Gardens, Edinburgh 3.

© *Crown Copyright* 1969

Published by
HER MAJESTY'S STATIONERY OFFICE

To be purchased from
13A Castle Street Edinburgh EH2 3AR
49 High Holborn, London W.C.1
109 St. Mary Street, Cardiff CF1 1JW
Brazennose Street, Manchester M60 8AS
50 Fairfax Street, Bristol BS1 3DE
258 Broad Street, Birmingham 1
7 Linenhall Street, Belfast BT2 8AY
or through any Bookseller

Printed in Scotland for Her Majesty's Stationery Office
by McCorquodale & Co. Ltd., Glasgow   K.68   Dd.131863

SBN 11 490247 X